This Is a Flower

The prickly poppy

This Is a Flower

ROSS E. HUTCHINS

Photographs by the author

DODD, MEAD & COMPANY

NEW YORK

TO LUCY PUCKETT,
who loves flowers and marvels at their mysteries

Introduction

This is the story of flowers, from the primitive kinds that once nodded beside prehistoric streams to those that bloom in your garden. On the pages that follow are recorded the remarkable features of pollination and the ways in which insects and other small creatures carry the precious "flower dust" from bloom to bloom. Sometimes, as we shall see, these creatures are unwilling helpers of the flowers and must be tricked into lending their services. Sometimes, too, this "flower dust" or pollen rides on the wind from flower to flower and from tree to tree.

The story of flowers is also, in many ways, the story of man's passage through history. During the thirty-year Wars of the Roses these flowers served as symbols of the warring factions. Flowers have entered our language in a thousand different ways and help to give it color and meaning. Down the centuries they have added touches of beauty to man's daily life, and he watched their opening and closing, often seeing therein dark omens and portents. People have usually considered flowers to have been created especially for human enjoyment, little realizing that the colorful blooms had the very practical purpose of bringing about pollination and seed production for the continuation of the species.

Most flowers open their faces to the sun, but there are many kinds that open only at dusk or in darkness and breathe out their heavy fragrance to attract night-flying moths. Some flowers bloom in the spring while others bloom only in summer or autumn. How do they "know" when the time has come for their debuts? Do they have built-in calendars and clocks?

Each year around the world flowers bloom in infinite variety. Regardless of the comings and goings of men and the problems they create for themselves, this yearly pageant will recur again and again as surely as the endless cycle of the seasons. This gives our lives stability because it is unchangeable. Long ago flowers bloomed for the ancient cave man just as they also bloom for you.

This is their story.

— R. E. H.

Contents

Introduction   7

1. What Is a Flower?   13
2. By Their Colors and Shapes   27
3. Trick or Treat   43
4. Gone with the Wind   59
5. Golden Dust   71
6. A Time to Bloom   85
7. Flower Perfumes   101
8. Along the Pathways of Time   111
9. For Each a Name   121
10. Their Family Tree   135

Index   149

This Is a Flower

This May-apple flower is a typical bloom. The bottle-shaped pistil is at the center. Its enlarged base is the ovary in which are located the ovules or developing seeds. The "cap" of the pistil is the stigma upon which pollen is deposited for pollination. Surrounding the pistil are the stamens with their pollen-filled anthers. White petals surround the pistil and stamens.

CHAPTER 1

What Is a Flower?

*L*ong ago people believed that flowers were placed on earth solely for human enjoyment. It apparently never occurred to them that the colorful blooms had any practical value to the plants themselves. Flowers, in most cases, are beautiful structures that add touches of color to the world's forests, jungles, deserts, prairies and gardens, but it is certainly not for their beauty alone that the plants produce them. Flowers are the end result of a plant's growth processes. A typical flower begins as a seed, and all the wonderful developmental and growth processes that occur have but one ultimate purpose—to assure the continuation of that particular kind of plant.

Some plants sprout from the seed, grow, flower and produce more seeds all in one year. We call such plants *annuals.* Other plants, such as beets and cabbages, require two growing seasons to complete the cycle. These are called *biennials.* The first summer these plants do not usually bloom. They merely store up food one summer and bloom the next. There is a third type of plant that grows for several years, blooming and producing seed each year or sometimes at the end of several years. Most of these plants die down to the ground each winter in cold climates and come up again the following season. Such plants are called *perennials,* common examples being rhubarb, peony, dahlia and rose. Included here also is the so-called century plant or *Agave.*

People used to think that this plant bloomed only after a hundred years of growth, but the truth is that it sends up a tall flowering stalk at the end of about ten years. After blooming, the plant dies.

While the most common means by which plants reproduce themselves is by the production of seeds, preceded by the flowering processes, there is another important reproductive method used by plants. This is called vegetative reproduction, a common example being the growth of new plants from cuttings and "slips." This is a common practice in greenhouses. It is easily possible to grow many common plants by placing stem, twig, or even leaf cuttings in moist sand and allowing them to take root. If you would like to experiment along this line, it is suggested that you try one of the new root growth-promoting chemicals such as *indoleascetic* or *indolebutyric* acid. These can be obtained from a seed dealer or dealer in garden supplies. Perhaps the easiest plants to root are willow twigs.

Many plants have lost their abilities to produce flowers and

Many plants, such as this sweet potato, are able to reproduce themselves vegetatively. *They do not need to produce seed; instead, new plants grow from the tubers.*

Bryophyllums reproduce themselves vegetatively by growing tiny plantlets along the edges of their leaves which produce roots, drop to the ground, and grow.

seeds and can be grown only by the vegetative method described above. Irish potatoes and sweet potatoes do sometimes produce seeds, but farmers ordinarily plant crops of these plants by cutting the tubers up into sections and planting these instead of seeds. Sprouts grow from the "eyes." The common banana is another example of a plant that is grown from tuber-like *rhizomes* or underground stems. The same is also true of both canna and iris.

It is usually much faster to reproduce plants vegetatively; for example, certain lilies can be grown vegetatively in a short time, whereas many years would be required to grow them from seeds. There are a number of plants that normally reproduce themselves vegetatively in nature. You may have noticed how strawberry plants put out "runners" at the ends of which new plants develop. In another plant, *Bryophyllum*, tiny plantlets grow in the leaf notches and when the leaves drop off, these plantlets take root and grow.

To the flower grower and the farmer there are certain other advantages in using vegetative methods of planting flowers and crop plants, the chief one being that a plant that grows from a cutting or "slip" is exactly like the plant from which the cutting or "slip" was obtained. On the other hand, when a plant is grown from a seed there is apt to be a blending of the characteristics of two different parent plants since, as we shall see, cross-pollination usually occurs.

Although some plants are not dependent upon seeds to reproduce themselves, we are concerned here with flowers and how they work to fulfill their destinies. The story of flowers and of flower pollination is probably the most fascinating in all nature.

But before we delve into the ways of flowers, we should learn something about how flowers are formed and about their parts. A typical flower is formed at the tip of a special stalk or "twig," the flower arrangement being one of several types. Each plant has its own characteristic style of flower arrangement. Beginning at the base of our typical flower are the leaflike *sepals*. These are usually green, but in some cases are colored like the petals above them. In some flowers, like pokeweed, four-o'clock, spurge nettle, pasque flower, and anemone, there are no petals, the colored sepals serving in their place. The same is true of poinsettia; the scarlet "petals" are actually bracts, or floral leaves, the true flowers being tiny structures at the center. This is also true of white dogwood flowers. In other flowers, such as fuchsia, iris, columbine and tulip, the sepals are colored like the petals and can only be identified as such by their location on the flower. Before flower buds open they are usually enclosed by the green sepals. You can observe these easily in a rosebud.

16

The "petals" of this dogwood bloom are actually sepals; *the petals are missing. The cluster of individual flowers is at the center. Poinsettias have a similar flower.*

The cup formed by the sepals is called the *calyx*. Just above the cup-like circle of sepals are the petals which are usually quite colorful and are what give the flower its characteristic appearance. The floral envelope formed by the petals is called the *corolla*. Flowers, as we shall see, come in almost every conceivable hue of the rainbow, and in many shapes.

Just inside the colored flower envelope or corolla are the *stamens* which bear the *anthers*. These constitute the male organs of the flower and there may be many or few of these, depending on the kind of flower. The anthers are small containers

17

or capsules within which the pollen grains develop. Their most common color is yellow, and they open at the appropriate time to liberate their store of pollen. We come next to the *pistil*. This is the female organ and consists of a tip called the *stigma* which is usually somewhat enlarged. It is upon the stigma that pollen grains germinate, sending long pollen tubes down through the pistil to the enlarged *ovary* located in its basal portion. Within the ovary are contained the developing *ovules* or immature seeds, and it is here that fertilization occurs upon entry of the pollen tube. Also, located somewhere within the flower, there are usually a number of nectar glands which secrete the nectar so eagerly sought by bees and hummingbirds.

Most flowers follow this basic structural plan, and a flower having all of the above organs is called a *perfect* flower; that is, it contains both male and female parts. Not all flowers are per-

A typical bloom is the huge magnolia which is six to eight inches in diameter. Its snowy petals surround the cluster of pistils and stamens. These blooms depend upon beetles for pollination.

This close-up of the central flower parts of the magnolia shows the numerous curled stigmas and, below, the stamens.

fect. For example, in the case of corn the male organs or stamens are contained in the tassels at the top of the stalk while the "ear" contains only the pistils and ovaries or female organs. Flowers like this are called *imperfect* flowers, and this condition is also found in oak, walnut and box elder. Most flowers, however, contain both male and female parts, or stamens and pistils, and are, thus, perfect flowers. Common examples of perfect flowers are daisies, sunflowers, buttercups and roses.

There are other cases in which the male and female blooms are borne on separate plants, the male blooms on one plant and the female blooms on another. In other words, there are both male and female plants. Common examples are cottonwoods, willows, poplars, ginkgoes and members of the holly family. Naturally, fruit is produced only on the female plant in these cases. Many people cannot understand why a certain tree or shrub in their garden blooms but never produces berries or fruit. The reason is that the tree or shrub in question is a male and contains only male blooms which produce no fruit.

The flower parts described above are usually arranged in a circle with the pistil or pistils at the center. The number of these parts in a flower is of great importance in plant classification. A botanist who sets out to identify an unknown plant must usually study the flower before he can determine what kind of plant he has. In many instances it is impossible to identify a plant unless the flower is present.

The plant kingdom is divided into the parallel-veined plants having leaves with parallel veins, and the net-veined plants having leaves with a net-like vein arrangement. Examples of parallel-veined plants are iris, lily, orchid and grass. Examples of net-veined plants are oak, magnolia, sunflower and pea. If we closely observe the blooms of these plants, we find that the parallel-veined plants bear flowers having their organs in threes or multiples of three. This can be seen easily if you examine an iris bloom. In this flower you can count three sepals, three petals, three stamens and a three-parted ovary. In the case of the net-veined plant tribe, on the other hand, the flower parts are arranged in fours or fives or multiples of these numbers. For example, a bloom of this type may have five sepals, five petals, ten stamens and a five-parted ovary. Or it may be the evening primrose which has four sepals, four petals, eight stamens and a four-parted ovary. These differences in flower structure help botanists to classify plants.

The brightly colored petals and other flower parts are like signboards that advertise to insects and hummingbirds that pollen and nectar are available. These bright colors are very important to the plant's survival as a species. For seeds to be

The lily is a typical flower of the plants with parallel-veined leaves. This lily has six stamens and a central pistil. The ovary can just be seen between the bases of the stamens.

produced by most plants it is first necessary that a transfer of pollen take place, involving the transfer of pollen from anthers, or the male part of a flower, to the stigmas, or female part, of the same flower or of another flower of the same kind. This, of course, is the basis of flower fertilization—the union of the two opposite sexes. Plants, unlike animals which have legs or wings and can move about, are unable to fly or walk and must have outside help in the transfer of their pollen. This is where wind, insects and birds enter the scene as helpers of the flowers.

Transfer of pollen is called *pollination* and may occur within the same flower, between different flowers on the same plant or between flowers on separate plants of the same kind. In the latter case the process is called *cross-pollination*. Cross-pollination is very important to most plants and results in increased variability in the species, enabling them to adapt themselves better to new conditions of growth. It usually results, too, in greater vigor of the new plant generation and in the production of more seeds or fruit.

The transfer of pollen from the male to the female parts of the same flower or between these parts on separate flowers on the same plant is called *self-pollination* and occurs normally in many plants, including wheat, rice, peas, cotton, and tomatoes. In some flowers, such as orchids, only cross-pollination occurs, the stigmas being poisonous to pollen from the same plant. Yet some plants such as peas depend wholly upon self-pollination. Most flowers, however, are cross-pollinated, and many common kinds are actually self-sterile. That is, when they are pollinated by their own pollen nothing happens. Some varieties of apples, to produce fruit, must receive pollen from another tree of a different variety. To produce seed, red clover blooms must receive pollen from another red clover plant, and this can only be accomplished with the help of bumblebees. It is estimated that there are no less than 3,000 plants whose flowers are self-sterile. Cross-pollinated flowers depend upon wind, insects or sometimes birds or other animals to carry their pollen from one flower to another.

Now, as you might guess, no insect is going to go to the trouble of gathering pollen from one flower and carrying it to another unless it is "paid" in some fashion for its services. Nature has taken care of this matter of payment for services rendered in several different ways, and the relationships between the flowers and their insect helpers are truly amazing. Some insects such as bees are paid off in pollen which is very nutritious and is carried

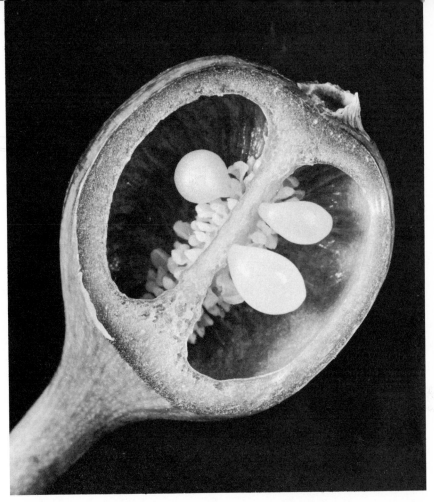

This narcissus seed pod or ovary shows three developing seeds and many ovules that failed to develop through lack of pollination.

back to the hive or nest to be fed to the young bees. The flowers merely produce enough extra pollen so that there is plenty left over after the pollination of other flowers to "pay" the bees for their services. Both honeybees and bumblebees have special pollen baskets located on their hind legs in which they can transport large quantities of pollen. As these insects fly from flower to flower filling their baskets, they more or less accidentally deposit some of this pollen on the stigmas or female parts of other blooms. This, of course, brings about cross-pollination. It is an interesting fact that honeybees usually gather pollen from but one kind of flower at a time. If the bees were to collect

Bumblebees probe into flowers for nectar. Here a bumblebee worker is sipping nectar from a zinnia.

pollen from miscellaneous flowers on one trip, much of that pollen would be wasted on flowers of other kinds where it would accomplish nothing. The way in which insects and flowers cooperate to their mutual advantage is quite remarkable.

But flowers also pay off their helpers in another way. Many flowers—perhaps the majority—also possess nectar glands which secrete sugary nectar that is eagerly sought by many bees and butterflies as well as hummingbirds. This nectar is rich in sugars and is highly nutritious. In the case of bees, it is gathered by being pumped into a special "honey stomach" through their mouthparts and transported back to the hive where it is placed in the wax cells and manufactured into honey. The honey, in turn, is used as food by both young and adult bees. We, also, take advantage of the honeybees' stores of honey, it having been used as human food since very ancient times.

In the process of gathering flower nectar, insects and birds accidentally become dusted with pollen grains and in going from flower to flower this pollen is brushed off upon the stigmas. Just as a bee visits only one kind of flower on a foraging trip when collecting pollen, Nature has "trained" the bees to do this same thing in collecting nectar. Thus, again, the flowers are assured that their pollen will not be wasted. In many flowers, as we shall see, there are quite amazing devices that prevent insects from obtaining nectar without also being well dusted with pollen. Some flowers use some quite unfair tricks and ingenious devices to obtain pollination services from unsuspecting insects. Strangest of all, perhaps, are some pitcher plants whose leaves are adapted for capturing and digesting insects but which also depend upon these same insects to help carry their pollen.

The tiny blooms of the huckleberry are shaped like bells. This shape helps to protect their pollen from rain.

CHAPTER 2

By Their Colors and Shapes

$\mathcal{F}$lowers grow in almost every conceivable shape and color. They vary in size from the tiny blooms of the bluets to the strange flowers of the parasitic *Rafflesia* plant, which are often three feet across and weigh fifteen pounds. These giant-sized plants grow in certain places in the Tropics, but the bloom of our native rose mallow may sometimes grow to be a foot across.

There is also, in the jungles of Sumatra, a giant arum with blooms ten feet tall. These huge plants are first cousins of our little jack-in-the-pulpits. Probably the smallest flower in the world is that of the duckweeds, tiny plants only one-eighth of an inch across. These pigmy plants are commonly found floating on the quiet waters of lakes and ponds.

Somewhere in the world there is probably a flower of almost any shape and color your mind can imagine. They come in crosses, globes, discs, trumpets, and triangles, as well as combinations of these. Nature has sometimes changed the shapes of individual petals and other flower parts so that they resemble birds, butterflies, bees or even starfish. The orchid tribe, especially, goes in for weird and beautiful forms. Seemingly, Nature has never let herself be hampered by any kind of rules in the designing of her blooms.

Most flower colors have their origin in the same chemical substances that give autumn leaves their bright hues. The accumulation of sugars in the plant tissues favors the formation of pigments called *anthocyanins* (meaning "blue flower"). In the case of autumn leaves, these pigments impart brilliant shades, not only of blue, but of gold, orange, red and even purple. Many flowers also contain these pigments. They give apples and peaches their rosy hues and roses their rich reds. They also give poinsettias and cardinal flowers their brilliant scarlets. These amazingly versatile pigments are dissolved in the cell sap and are also responsible for the deep red of beets. The anthocyanins are sensitive to acid or alkaline conditions and may change color when changed from an alkaline to an acid condition or vice versa. For example, the flowers of the common chicory are blue when they first open, but as acid residues accumulate in the petals they change to pink. And there is a flower in the West Indies called the Changeable Rose. Actually, it is a mallow or *Hibiscus,* but the remarkable thing about it is that when it first opens it is snow white, the color soon changing to rose-color and then to purple. The bloom runs through this color range within a few hours.

The anthocyanins add color to some flowers in another way, too. If we look at a purple tulip petal under a microscope, we find that some cells contain red pigment while others contain blue pigment. When the flower is viewed with the unaided eye, however, the red and blue colors blend together and the flower looks purple. An eighteenth century artist named Seurat used this same technique in blending the colors in his paintings. He found that by using tiny dots of pure colors he could obtain the shades he wished since the eye tended to blend the dots together. He also found that by varying the distance between the colored dots he could create various tones. Seurat's method of painting was called Pointillism, which was a form of Impressionism. In the case of many flowers the petal color is not the result of either tiny points of different colors or of solid colors but of different colors placed one above the other within the

28

petal tissues. The coloration of some autumn leaves, also, is the result of this same principle.

Most of us are familiar with the fact that hydrangeas may be either pink or blue and sometimes the same plant may bear blooms of both colors. Recent experiments have shown that when pink hydrangeas are sprayed with an aluminum compound they change to blue. It has been known for a long while that hydrangeas grown in an alkaline soil are usually pink while an acid soil imparts a blue color to them. It has also been found that alkaline soils contain very little iron or aluminum while acid soils contain a good deal. Thus, the color of hydrangeas comes back to the question of how much iron or aluminum is present in the soil in which the plants grow. Apparently, however, the flower color is more dependent upon the aluminum than on the iron content of the soil.

The green color of all plants is dependent upon the presence of the wonder substance called *chlorophyll* that occurs as microscopic granules inside most plant cells. Chlorophyll has the unique ability of being able to manufacture sugars and starch from water and gas from the air with the aid of sunshine. Some plants, such as mushrooms, do not contain this green chlorophyll. In this case, however, the plant does not manufacture its own food but lives upon dead organic matter in the soil. Now contained within the green granules of chlorophyll there are some other substances that apparently help it to do its work of food manufacture. These are the *xanthophylls* (meaning "leaf yellow") and *carotene* (derived from the Latin word for carrot). These are yellow, orange or sometimes red pigments, and they, too, add color to autumn forests. Many common flowers, also, receive their colors from these substances, which are especially abundant in yellow flowers such as dandelions, zinnias, sunflowers and goldenrods. Oranges, lemons, tomatoes and rose hips are tinted by these same versatile pigments, and they are also found in carrots, egg yolks and butter. One of these pigments,

The color patterns of pansies guide bees in to a landing on the lower petal. The nectar chamber is reached through opening at center.

called *lycopene,* gives watermelons and pink grapefruit their red coloration.

So much for the bright colors of flowers, but what about white flowers? The white "color" of most plants, including flower petals, results when there is no pigment at all. Sometimes the white is more striking if air spaces are present in the plant tissues causing light rays to scatter. This same thing is true of white bird feathers which are filled with tiny air spaces. It might be mentioned in passing that many of the most brilliant colors of birds, especially blue and metallic hues, are the result of feather structure rather than the presence of actual pigments or colored substances. The microscopic structure of the feathers breaks the

The central corolla tube of the narcissus extends out from the bloom. Flying insects use it as a target in landing on the flower.

light rays up into colored rays somewhat like tiny prisms do. If, for example, you were to grind up a blue bluejay feather into a fine powder, you would find that the powder was not blue but gray or black. There is no real blue color or pigment present. These are called *structural* colors, and they are also responsible for many of the most brilliant hues of butterfly wings.

In our daily lives all of us are guided—or attempts are made to guide us—to stores, restaurants or highways by means of arrows and other signs, neon and otherwise. These visual lures are so common that we think nothing about them, yet they often help us to find what we are looking for. In a sense, all flowers are signboards that advertise the fact that either pollen, nectar, or both are available to insects or birds for a small price. The price, of course, is the accidental depositing of a small part of the collected pollen on other flowers. Nectar may be considered as an outright gift to entice insects and birds to the flowers. Of course, neither the bees, nor the butterflies nor the hummingbirds know that they are also helping the flowers when they fly from flower to flower collecting nectar or pollen for food.

In order for these flower signboards to attract insects, they must, of course, be seen by them, and that is the reason for flower color. The eyes of insects are not "built" like our eyes, and they are able to see colors that are invisible to us. For example, *ultraviolet* is invisible to us but quite visible to insects. It is also a fact that most insects are attracted more to colors at the blue end of the spectrum than at the red end. You may recall that when a beam of sunlight passes through a glass prism it is separated into its various colors, ranging from red through orange and yellow, to green, blue and violet. This is called the sun's *spectrum.* I once made some experiments on the attractiveness of colored lights to night-flying insects and found that far more insects were attracted to blue lights than to red lights. Other biologists have found the same thing to be true, and that insects are also attracted to ultraviolet light which the human eye cannot see at all. On the other hand, it is probable that most insects are color-blind to deep red, which may account for the fact that many flowers that are red depend on hummingbirds for pollination instead of insects. There are few red flowers in Europe and Asia where hummingbirds do not occur. Hummingbirds, as you may know, are found only in North and South America, being especially abundant in South America, a land where numerous red and scarlet flowers abound. It is a fact, too, that when the Mexican century plant, which has hummingbird-pollinated flowers, is grown in Europe it produces no seed. Hummingbirds seem necessary to its fertility. Bees, like most other insects, are not usually very enthusiastic about red blooms,

This is a close-up of a honeybee's eye. If you look closely you can see that it is composed of hundreds of tiny "eyes." Each is a complete visual organ and probably sees a separate image. All insects have these compound eyes. The hairs covering the eye probably do not interfere with vision.

since they cannot distinguish red from black or gray. You will find that most flowers that depend upon bees for pollination are yellow or blue. These include such flowers as larkspur, snapdragon, peas, and violets. Another example is the monkshood which depends upon bumblebees and does not occur outside the normal range of these insects. Butterflies, however, are often attracted to flowers such as red butterfly weed. They are not color-blind to red as are bees.

The eyes of insects are composed of many hundreds of small eyes, each an entirely separate visual organ. Just how an insect sees through these *compound* eyes we do not really know even though photographs can be taken through them. When a picture

Is this how a daisy looks to a bee? This picture was actually made through an insect's eye by an ingenious apparatus.

is photographed through an insect's eye a multiple image is obtained (see photo above), but for all we know the many images may be combined into one image in the insect's brain just as the images of our two eyes are combined into one. In any case, this type of vision is called *mosaic* vision and is probably especially effective in perceiving motion. As proof of this, it has been found that bees settle more readily on flowers during windy days than on still days when there is no flower movement.

Honeybees can be trained to come to flowers of a certain color. This is done by arranging a number of discs of various colors in a row. On one of these colored discs is placed a glass dish of honey. After the bees have learned that the honey is on this disc, the honey is moved to another disc. The bees still go to the colored disc where the honey was first located. In this way the color preferences of honeybees have been determined.

Studies have been made to find what it is that attracts insects and hummingbirds to flowers, and it has been discovered that to honeybees odor or perfume is most important beyond a range of about thirty feet. It is only when bees are closer than this that the colors and shapes of flowers become important. There is a great deal of difference in various insects' senses of smell and vision. Bees seem to have the best vision. Next in line come butterflies, and moths and beetles follow, in that order. Hummingbirds, of course, have eyes similar to our own and can spot flowers a hundred yards or so away. Large fields of flowers, of course, can be located by bees long distances away by odor alone.

In general it may be said that the colors of flowers tend to contrast with their backgrounds. The flowers of tall day-blooming cacti, for example, are usually yellow and yellow stands out best against the blue sky of the desert. Of course, there are always exceptions to any rule one may make. It is obvious that the color of many flowers makes them stand out against the green foliage of the plants on which they grow. Such flowers may be white, yellow, red or blue. But some flowers bloom in early spring before leaves unfold, and many of these are yellow or white. Trailing flowers that bloom down near the ground are often white. This is true of the tiny blooms of the twinflower and of the mountain spurge or *Pachysandra*.

Any flying creature is faced with the problems of navigation just as an airplane pilot is. A carrier-plane pilot needs signalmen and painted marks on the flight deck of the ship to guide him in to a safe landing, and flowers, too, provide guides or targets for their flying insect or bird friends. A number of blue flowers have yellow clusters of stamens at their centers that probably serve

This daisy is a good example of a "target" flower. It is composed of many individual flowers or florets, but only the outer "flowers" have petals. Thus, one row of petals serves many flowers.

this purpose. Some varieties of yellow narcissus have outer edges of their flower tubes painted dark red. This makes an ideal target for the guidance of bees. If you examine a number of pansy blooms you will notice that the color patterns of their "faces" seem to guide the eye to their centers. The ox-eye daisy with its dark center surrounded by yellow petals is a fine example of a target flower. Another common example is the zinnia.

These target patterns and nectar guides take many forms. Sometimes the flower disc is marked by conspicuous radiating lines that converge toward the center where the pollen and nectar are stored. There are a number of flowers, also, in which there are "landing strips" of contrasting color on their lower lips where bees ordinarily alight. Such flowers are certainly providing their insect helpers with a designated strip or platform on which to land. The insects are receiving the "red carpet treatment." If you will examine a number of flowers, both wild and cultivated, you will see quite a number of these markings that quite obviously were designed by Nature to serve as navigational aids to flying insects, and, perhaps, to hummingbirds.

The shapes of flowers, too, apparently have a great deal to do with their attractiveness to insects. A scientist in Germany found that bees could distinguish between gentian-shaped and sunflower-shaped blooms but could not learn the difference between solid squares and triangles. This is reasonable when one realizes

Salvia blooms have little landing platforms for the convenience of their insect visitors.

Using artificial "flowers" like these, scientists found that bees could distinguish any of the flower shapes in the back row from any of those in the front row. They could not tell the difference between individual shapes in either row, but preferred the flower shapes in the front row.

that there are no square flowers in nature! This same scientist constructed a "flower garden" something like the one shown above. The back row of cardboard "flowers" consisted of a solid disc, a square, a triangle and a bar. The front row consisted of "flowers" having broken outlines. It was found that bees could not learn to distinguish between any of the "flowers" in the back row or between any of the "flowers" in the front row, but that they preferred any of the "flowers" in the front row over any of those in the back row. This is a most interesting bit of honeybee psychology. Bees are more attracted to flowers of complicated shapes than to flowers of simple forms.

Some flowers attract insects by their size, as do the three-foot blooms of the *Rafflesia* of the Tropics. But many of the larger flowers bloom at night, spreading their petals in dim light to serve as targets in luring night-flying insects. In such flowers the most common shade, naturally, is white since colors are not visible at night. The huge *Rafflesia* bloom, however, is dull colored, relying on its foetid odor to attract insects. In bright moonlight, colored objects all appear as shades of gray. Thus, in moonlight, insects as well as humans are color-blind, and flowers appear as if they had been photographed in black and white. One of the most spectacular of all our native blooms is that of the snowy queen-of-the-night cactus of Arizona. Then, of course, there is the night-blooming cereus, a cactus-like plant often grown in flower pots. Its large flowers usually begin opening at dusk and are fully expanded by midnight. They measure a foot across. I well remember a call I received from a lady at two o'clock one morning saying that her night-blooming cereus had just bloomed, and did I want to take pictures of it? I did not—not at 2:00 A.M.—and that is the reason no picture of this interesting flower is included in this book! When a number of these large blooms are open on the same plant the effect is very beautiful, however.

Many cacti are night bloomers and appeal to nocturnal insects by their snow-white color or by their heavy perfume. It is interesting, too, that most day-blooming cacti having brightly colored

Flowers of the night are usually white because only pale flowers are visible in dim light. The brightly colored blooms in this garden are not visible in the dusk.

flowers have little or no odor. Nature usually does not waste her efforts on anything that is not needed. With regard to the night-blooming cereus mentioned previously, the flowers which open only at night are white, but the mature fruits are bright red. This attracts birds that help to distribute the seeds.

Most of us are familiar with the white trumpet-like flowers of *Datura* or angel's-trumpet which slowly unfold at dusk to spread their heavy fragrance. These blooms attract many hawk moths that hover before them while probing into the deep throats with their long tube-like mouthparts. These are true flowers of the night and with the coming of dawn quickly wilt and eventually fall from the plant, their mission fulfilled. On the other hand, the large white flowers of the magnolia remain open all day and it is upon beetles that they depend for pollination.

In Germany there is a flower called the *Nacht Viole* or night violet. This flower is noted for its perfume and also for the fact that, in darkness, it emits sparks of light. Such luminous flowers have been reported since very early times. For instance, the

In many cases Nature arranges small flowers in clusters to increase their attractiveness to insects. This Queen Anne's lace is a good example.

daughter of the famous Swedish botanist, Carolus Linnaeus, once saw something that resembled tiny lightning flashes in nasturtium flowers during a warm, stormy night. More than a hundred years ago a man in England noticed that some marigolds were luminous, and another man noted little lightning flashes in red poppies. Such flashes have also been seen on or near tuberoses, sunflowers and evening primroses. Just what the scientific explanation of these lights is no one seems to know. Perhaps some volatile substance such as essential oil evaporating from flowers on warm nights ignites on contact with the air. Anyway, these spark-like flashes that have often been seen in and around flowers remain one of the minor riddles of botany.

There are many flowers that depend upon moths of the dusk or night, a few examples being morning-glory, tobacco, yucca, and many orchids. Many of these moth flowers have deep throats that can only be reached by the long tongues of hawk moths. In some cases the nectar is contained in long spurs where the moths obtain it with their tongues which may be several inches long. In some cases, bumblebees have learned the trick of robbing these flowers of their sweets by making slits in the sides of the nectar spurs and then inserting their tongues. This occurs in both larkspurs and columbines.

Many plants with small blooms compensate for their small size by massing them together into bunches or clumps to make them more conspicuous.

Thus, we see that there are colorful day flowers and pale night flowers and that each has its own special visitors. By day there are the sun-loving butterflies, bees and hummingbirds, but at dusk a new "shift" takes over to carry on the work of nectar sipping and pollination. In Nature's scheme of things each has its time and place.

Pussywillows have no colorful petals to advertise their nectar, but they are gener-ous with their pollen.

CHAPTER 3

Trick or Treat

*I*n all the world of plants there is probably nothing more remarkable than the tricks used by many plants to secure the help of insects in carrying pollen. You would have a hard time thinking of a method of pollen transfer that some plant somewhere in the world does not use. It is also a safe bet that many of these tricks are so clever that you would never have thought of them at all. But Nature has had plenty of time to develop techniques, so it is not at all surprising that in a hundred million years she should have come up with some ingenious methods of cross-pollination.

Offhand, it would seem a simple matter for flowers to obtain the services of insects in transporting their golden pollen. Seemingly, all that should be needed is a supply of nectar and pollen to reward insects for their services, and colorful blooms and scents to advertise their location. In the case of many flowers it is just that simple, but in other flowers the matter is much more complicated. Suppose, for example, that at the period when a flower blooms there are no insects on the wing, as is often the case during cool or rainy weather. If pollination of some sort does not occur, these plants will produce no seeds at all. Adverse weather conditions at a critical season could thus wipe out all the flowering plants in an entire region. But Nature, as usual, has taken steps to see that this does not occur.

We have seen that cross-pollination is very important to plants, and that this is usually the aim of most flowers. Still, it is a fact that these plants can survive for many generations through self-pollination, having their flowers fertilized by their own pollen. There are many flowers that offer their wares to insects and, if there are none available, they then pollinate their own flowers as a last resort.

Take the case of the shooting star, for example. These attractive flowers lure bees which will accomplish cross-pollination, but if no bees arrive, then the anthers of the flowers eventually drop their pollen upon the stigma, bringing about self-pollination. There are other flowers that simply close up each night and reopen again the next day and by continuing this process

Passion flowers entice bees with both nectar and pollen. Note the filled pollen basket on this honeybee's hind leg.

Many of the our brightest flowers are butterfly-pollinated. Here a giant swallowtail sips nectar from a yellow zinnia.

cross-pollination finally occurs. In other cases the stamens are attached to the walls of the flower tube and, if cross-pollination fails, the flower tube simply falls off. As it falls off, the stamens with their pollen-filled anthers brush against the stigma, dusting it with pollen.

There are many tricks used by flowers that prevent self-pollination. In some plants, such as those of peppergrass, the stamens hide behind the petals so that they cannot touch the stigma. Later, if pollination has not already occurred, the stamens bend toward the stigma and dust it with pollen. In this way there is

45

a good chance that pollen from another plant will be deposited on the stigma before it receives its own pollen. In the case of the garden primrose there are two kinds of blooms. One kind has a short pistil and long stamens, while the other has a long pistil and short stamens. By this arrangement the chances of insects becoming dusted with pollen from one bloom and carrying it to another are greatly increased. Some flowers have carried these differences in stamen and pistil lengths to even greater extremes. The spiked loosestrife is a good example of this. The blooms of this plant are magenta in color and are of three kinds, each having stamens and pistils of different lengths. The pollen, also, is colored differently. Healthy seed results only when pollen from the long stamens is deposited upon other blooms with long pistils. Likewise, pollination is most effective when pollen is carried from medium length stamens to medium length pistils, or from short stamens to short pistils. The insects involved in this complicated cross-pollination are chiefly butterflies.

One of the most common tricks used to prevent self-pollination is that of having anthers and stigmas mature at different times. In these cases the stigmas are ready to receive pollen before the anthers are shedding it, or the other way around. This arrangement makes self-pollination virtually impossible. Some flowers have simplified matters by having their stigmas poisonous to their own pollen.

Another trick that promotes cross-pollination is often found in flowers. Stamens and pistils switch positions so that only one or the other at a time will be directly in the path of insect visitors. These changes in position of the flower parts are brought about by slow movements and can only be detected if you observe them at intervals. In this way the insects are dusted with pollen in one flower and brush it off on the stigma of another flower. This phenomenon occurs in many common flowers including many gentians, mallows, the monkshood, gladiolus, salvia (sage), nightshade and some honeysuckles.

Flower motion helps to attract bees and other insects. The blooms of wild morning-glories are suspended on coiled, springlike stems, causing them to twist rapidly back and forth in the slightest air movement. One of these unusual flowers is shown here. Two seed pods are at the left.

There are some flowers whose anthers move very rapidly to make sure that insect visitors are well dusted. A good example is the prickly pear cactus, in which the anthers bend toward any insect that comes. A somewhat similar trick is employed by the barberry bloom. The stamens of this flower normally rest out against the petals, but when touched by a bee they move inward, smearing it with a bit of pollen. The bee, of course, is apt to visit other barberry flowers where this pollen is brushed off upon the stigmas. Mountain laurel blooms have an even better arrangement. In this case, the anthers are held fast in tiny pouches in the petals. When an insect touches these stamens they snap inward toward the center of the flower, dusting the insect. In the event that there are no insect visitors, the stamens remain hidden in their petal pockets until the bloom withers.

One would hardly expect to find much of interest behind the pensive "face" of a pansy, yet within this common bloom is found one of the neatest of flower tricks. In order to understand the mechanisms of the pansy flower, study the photograph of the cross-section on page 49. If you look closely at the "face" of a pansy you will see, at the center, a small opening within which is a knob-like structure. This is the stigma. When a butterfly or bee approaches the bloom, guided by its color pattern, it alights and thrusts its *proboscis* or nectar-sucking tube into the opening beneath the globular stigma. If the insect has previously visited another pansy there probably are some pollen grains adhering to the proboscis and these are scooped up into a small cavity in the knob-like stigma where pollination then occurs. The insect pushes its proboscis on into the flower, reaching the hollow spur at the back. This contains a tiny pool of nectar and, when the supply has been drained, the proboscis is withdrawn. When the proboscis is withdrawn, however, a number of pollen grains, which have fallen from the cone of anthers behind the stigma, stick to it. When the insect flies away it unknowingly carries this pollen and deposits it in the stigma of the next pansy it visits.

This cross-section of a pansy bloom shows the clever method used to assure cross-pollination. When an insect pushes its beak into the flower beneath the knoblike stigma any adhering pollen is rubbed off in the tiny depression. After the insect has drunk its fill from the nectar pool at the back, it withdraws its beak, carrying fresh pollen with it. This is carried away to other pansy blooms.

*An azalea bloom holds its stamens and pistil out into
the path of any insects that may come seeking nectar.*

Thus, the insect—bee or butterfly—pays for its dinner by cross-pollinating the pansies.

A somewhat different method of tricking insects is used by the common nasturtium. If you look this flower in the "face" you will see four petals. Extending out between these four petals are the stamens bearing the pollen-filled anthers. Beneath the bloom are four nectar-filled spurs. When a bee alights upon the flower and thrusts its proboscis down into a nectar spur, one side of its head touches an anther and becomes smeared with pollen while the other side touches the stigma. Since the bee

50

usually crawls around inside the flower, thrusting its proboscis into one nectar spur after another, the same side of its head continues to touch the anthers. Thus, it will have one side of its head smeared with pollen from all four anthers. Now when it flies to another nasturtium bloom there is a fifty-fifty chance that it will move around the flower in the opposite direction, rubbing the pollen-smeared side of its head against the stigma, covering it with pollen from the previous bloom. At the same time the other side of its head is being dusted with pollen from the anthers of this second flower. In this way there is a good chance that if several flowers are visited, pollen will be transferred from the anther of one to the stigma of another and cross-pollination is accomplished.

There are several flowers, including catalpa, monkey flower and bladderwort, that have "invented" still another means of preventing self-pollination. The stigmas of these flowers are split into two lip-like structures. When ready to receive pollen the stigmas extend out into the path of any insects which may enter the flower. These lips are spread wide apart, and any pollen on the insects is brushed off upon the lower lip which then closes. The pollen-bearing anthers are farther inside the bloom so the insects do not come in contact with them until they have already passed the stigma lips and rubbed pollen from other flowers off on them. By the time the insect is ready to leave the flower, the lips have closed and any pollen picked up from the anthers cannot be left on the stigmas. Self-pollination is impossible. If you have some of these flowers and care to experiment, try touching their lip-like stigmas with a needle. You will see how fast the stigma lips close.

There is a flower in Persia, known by the scientific name of *Crucianella*, which belongs to the Madder family. These flowers are small and trumpet-like and grow in clusters. While the bloom is still closed a tension builds up inside, and when any insect alights upon it the petals suddenly pop open and pollen is exploded into the air, covering the insect. The insect then flies to blooms that are already open where some of this pollen is rubbed off upon the stigmas. Our own paper mulberry and some other flowers also have mechanisms for "exploding" pollen into the air or onto insects.

Water is the enemy of almost all pollen. It is, thus, only natural that aquatic or water plants should be faced with special problems. One water plant has solved the pollination problem in a very clever way. This is the common aquarium plant called ribbon grass or *Vallisneria*. These plants grow completely submerged, but during summer they produce small male and female flowers. The male flower is, of course, filled with pollen, but it is contained within tiny waterproof spheres. The female flowers, on the other hand, are located at the ends of long, slender filaments that grow upward and eventually reach the surface. Here they open and await pollination. In the meantime, the submerged male flowers liberate their pollen-filled spheres which bob to the surface. At the surface of the water these spheres open into the form of tiny pollen-filled boats which drift about until they come in contact with one of the female flowers. Pollination then occurs, after which the slender stem of the female flower coils up like a spiral spring, pulling the flower back beneath the water where the fruit develops safe from enemies. Certainly, this is an ingenious solution to the pollination problem faced by a submerged plant.

Flowers are not really mechanical devices, yet some flowers have perfected very efficient lever systems to help in the distribution of their pollen. An outstanding example is found in the common salvia or sage bloom. As a bee enters this flower it encounters two levers, the longest ends of which curve up over the insect's back and bear the anthers at their tips. These levers are hinged near their lower ends. The nectar pockets, as usual, are located deep inside the flower. As the bee pushes into the floral tube in its effort to rob it of nectar, it comes in contact

52

with the lower ends of the levers and presses against them. This causes the long arms bearing the anthers to swing down and smear pollen on the bee's back.

Botanists have also discovered many clever pollination schemes among the orchids. For instance, in the *Listera* orchid the lower petal is long and lip-like with a groove down its center which is filled with nectar. When an insect alights upon this lip it at once begins lapping up the sweet nectar, crawling upward to obtain the last drop. When it reaches the top, however, it comes in contact with two sacs of pollen, called *pollinia*. Two minute drops of cement are exuded, which glue the two pollinia firmly to the insect's head. These pollinia are later rubbed off on another orchid.

The salvia bloom depends upon bees to transfer its pollen. As pay for their services the bees receive a sip of nectar from glands deep inside the flower.

The *Calopogon* orchid which grows in the eastern part of this country employs another trick. The upper petal of this pretty flower is the longest and bears many glandular hairs on its front surface. Apparently, some nectar is also present. Now when a bee alights upon this erect petal its weight causes the petal to flop over, placing the bee in an undignified upside-down position. While the bee is thus pinned down on the lower petal the orchid quickly cements four pollen sacs on its back.

Then consider the tricks of the common *Habenaria*, or fringed orchid, which ranges over most of the United States and northward to Alaska. The small greenish-white flowers grow along a stalk which arises between two leaves that spread flat upon the ground. In these small members of the orchid tribe, which are most apt to be found growing in damp woods, the lower petals are greatly elongated and strap-like. In fact, the botanical name *Habenaria* is derived from the Latin word *habena,* meaning "strap." The insect involved in this little drama is a moth and, like all moths, it carries its proboscis coiled up beneath its head like a watch spring. When it alights upon the convenient perch formed by the orchid's strap it inserts its proboscis into the deep throat in search of nectar. In the act of doing this, however, the moth's eyes come in contact with pollen sacs or pollinia located on either side of the floral tube. Here a pollen sac is firmly cemented to each of the moth's eyes. These sacs are on short stalks. Before the story of *Habenaria* pollination was known, these pollen sacs, sometimes found attached to moths' eyes, were believed to be some sort of abnormal growth or parasites. After the moth leaves the *Habenaria* bloom, the pollen sacs begin to droop on their short stalks and eventually hang down in such a position that when the moth visits another orchid they come in contact with the sticky stigma to which they become attached and pulled off the moth's eyes. In this way the orchid makes sure that its pollen will be transported to another bloom of the same kind.

Dutchman's pipe blooms have expanded chambers back of the flower opening. Insects are trapped here and held prisoner until they pollinate the flower. They are then released to fly to other Dutchman's pipe flowers where they are trapped again. Thus, cross-pollination is assured.

We now turn our attention from the orchid tribe to the strange flowers of the *Aristolochias* or Dutchman's pipes which also trap insects. There are several kinds of these flowers that thrive mostly in the Tropics, but, fortunately, some of the smaller ones grow in Florida and other warm parts of this country. The entrances to these blooms are more or less trumpet-shaped. Behind the expanded entrance is a narrow throat which may be curved or straight. The inner surface of this throat is lined with hairs which are directed backward. Behind this is an expanded chamber. The peculiar odor of the bloom, which in some cases resembles decaying meat, attracts numerous small flies which creep through the narrow throat and enter the enlarged chamber at the back. Here they are trapped since the hairs in the throat all point backward. At times so many flies become trapped that their buzzing is audible several feet away. As the tiny prisoners crawl and buzz about, any pollen adhering to them from previous Dutchman's pipe blooms is rubbed off onto the stigmas. At this stage, however, the anthers are not ready to shed their pollen, so the flies are held in their prison for about ten hours, or until the anthers shed their pollen. When this occurs the flies become dusted with pollen and the hairs that prevented their escape then wilt, allowing the prisoners to escape. They are soon trapped again, however, and held prisoner by other blooms, bringing about cross-pollination.

The blooms of the common milkweed have developed a most remarkable method of tricking insects into transporting pollen. Milkweeds are visited by many insects that come seeking nectar, but in one case, that of the monarch butterfly, the larvae also feed upon the succulent leaves. If you will take the trouble to examine a milkweed flower under a hand lens you will find that each of the blooms which constitute the flowering head consists of a central disc surrounded by five colored, hood-like nectaries. Below these nectaries are five petal-like sepals. Around the sides of the central disc—which is actually the stigma—there are five slits, one between each nectary. When a bee, or other insect, alights upon the flower one or more of its feet enters the lower ends of the slits. Now, when it has drained the flower of its nectar and attempts to fly away, its feet are pulled up through the slits. As this occurs, tiny wishbone-shaped devices become attached to the feet. These wishbone devices are actually pollen sacs or pollinia, and bees captured in fields of milkweeds may have several dozen of these tiny devices attached to their legs. When a bee having these paired pollen sacs clipped to its legs visits another milkweed, some of them become dislodged and remain in contact with the sticky stigma. Thus is pollination completed.

There are many strange plants in the world, but some of the strangest belong to the arum family. To this unusual group belong such "characters" as skunk cabbage, taro, jack-in-the-pulpit, calla lily, caladium, philodendron, voodoo lily, and, last but not least, the giant arum lily of Sumatra. This latter is the world's largest flower, often reaching a height of eight or ten feet, but it would certainly not take any prize for beauty. Like most arums, this giant among flowers is shaped something like a huge vase with a central stalk which contains the anthers and stamens. The vase-like portion is called the *spathe,* while the central column is called the *spadex.* Now the remarkable thing about this giant flower is that it smells, not like a lily, but like decaying meat, an odor which attracts numerous carrion beetles. These insects are trapped in the lower portion of the spathe or "vase" where they must remain until pollination has been accomplished.

Our native arums such as the attractive little jack-in-the-pulpits are really just miniatures of their giant relative in Sumatra. Many arum flowers generate considerable heat at the time of blooming. One biologist has studied heat production in the pretty voodoo lily and found that the heat begins developing within the flower about a day before it opens. The heat is believed to aid the flowers in volatilizing their odors. Another heat-producing flower is the unusual moonwort, a primrose that grows in the Swiss Alps. During winter its leathery leaves are buried under snow and ice, but with the coming of spring sufficient heat is developed in the plant to enable its flower buds to melt their way up through the ice and snow to the sun where its blue flowers are pollinated by bees.

So far we have dealt mainly with the relationships between flowers and insects. But birds, too, have their part to play in the drama of pollination. Here in our own country the common hummingbird often carries pollen, but in South America there are many different kinds of hummingbirds and many scarlet blooms that depend upon them. In South Africa there are a number of bird-pollinated flowers, such as the bird-of-paradise flower or *Strelitzia,* that depend upon small honey birds for pollination. On many of the islands of the Pacific Ocean there occur honey-creepers, small birds that seek the nectar of many flowers and thus bring about pollination.

Thus we see that insects and birds are often tricked into aiding the flowers, but they are usually treated to pollen and nectar as pay for their services.

This cut-away picture of a jack-in-the-pulpit shows the pistils deep inside the flower. The stamens are on the central column or spadex. Small flies enter from the top and are trapped until pollination occurs.

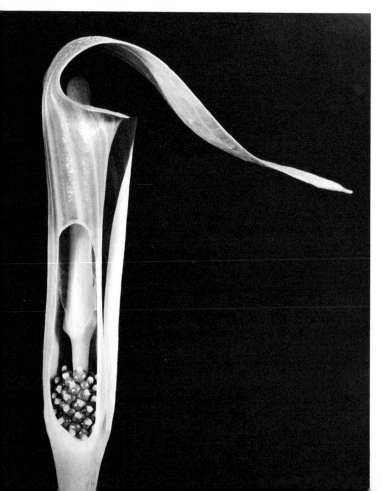

CHAPTER 4

Gone with the Wind

There are usually several different ways of doing almost anything. In modern times we cross the oceans in propeller-driven ships or by airplanes. Either of these types of transportation will get us where we wish to go. But it was not too long ago that men crossed the world's greatest oceans in sailing vessels that were driven by winds. The winds are great travelers, always on the move. With the help of these restless air currents that we call winds, many plants, too, have traveled to far lands and taken root there. Some plants travel to distant places by attaching parachutes to their seeds and floating them through the air. You have seen these parachute-bearing seeds, common examples being those of dandelions, thistles and milkweeds. If these seeds settle on fertile soil, new generations of plants arise far from the places where they originated. Many common plants have crossed oceans in this way.

Thus do plants take advantage of the winds as a means of transportation. But many plants use winds in another way. They send their pollen by "air mail" to other plants of the same kind and, thus, bring about cross-pollination and fertilization.

Most flowers, as we have seen, use the help of insects and birds for pollen transportation, but there was a time many millions of years ago when there were no such creatures. Before there were flying insects and birds, plants did not produce colorful blooms since there would have been no use for them. Flowers and insects and birds—especially flowers and insects—go together. Most biologists believe that the ancient plants that lived before there were birds and winged insects depended upon wind to carry their pollen. The remote ansectors of the pines depended upon winds just as modern pines do today. If you shake a small pine tree in spring when it is shedding its pollen, you will see a yellow cloud of pollen float away. In regions where there are extensive stands of pine this floating pollen often gives exposed objects a coating of yellow "dust," to the disgust of housewives.

Besides pines, there are many other plants and trees that still rely on winds to air-lift their pollen. Common examples are pop-

Millions of years ago there were no colorful flowers. Plants reproduced by spores as do these horsetails, or equisetums, *still living today. The spores are produced in the enlarged heads.*

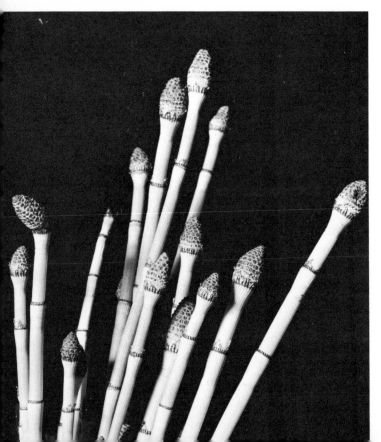

Pines produce abundant pollen which is carried away on the wind. These male catkins of pine were jarred, causing a golden shower of pollen to fall.

lar, birch, mulberry, alder, oak, hickory, grasses and corn. Corn, of course, is also a grass. Other wind-pollinated plants are hemp, hops, cattail, ragweed and plantain. Such plants and trees are said to be *anemophilous* which means "wind loving." All of the above plants depend mostly upon wind, but you will often find bees collecting their pollen, which may or may not be helping the plants since most wind-pollinated kinds have the two sexes located in separate flowers. The female flowers of wind-pollinated plants, of course, produce no pollen or nectar and, so, an insect would be unlikely to visit them and leave any pollen.

61

The anthers or pollen-bearing organs of corn are located at the top of the stalk, in the "tassels." The female organs are located in the "ear," and each silk is a stigma. Like all other grasses, corn is wind-pollinated.

The corn plant is a good example to study. The tassel is located at the top of the stalk and if you examine this structure closely you will find many tiny anthers suspended along its branches. If you have a magnifying glass, and the corn is at the right stage, you can see that each anther has a minute hole at its lower end. As the wind swings the anthers about, the pollen is shaken out, a little at a time, like salt out of a shaker. The moving air carries this dust-like pollen away and, if there are other corn plants growing nearby, it may alight on the exposed silks. These corn silks are actually the stigmas of the corn plant, and, if you trace a single silk down through the husk to the ear, you can see that it connects to one of the ovules or developing grains of corn. There is one silk attached to each grain. When a pollen grain alights upon the exposed tip of a silk it sends a pollen tube down through the silk to the ovule where fertilization occurs. Honeybees as well as other insects often feed upon or collect corn pollen from the tassels, but it is obvious that they are of no help in pollination since there is no reason for them to visit the silks also.

Other grasses besides corn are wind-pollinated, but in most instances the male and female flower parts are located close together. The pollination process is, however, about the same, except that the anthers and stigmas usually develop at different times on the same plant, thereby making self-pollination unlikely. The liberation of grass pollen is quite an interesting process to watch, but to see how it is done you will have to arise very early in the morning. Shortly after dawn the anthers begin expanding and pushing out of their sheaths. The movement is quite rapid and within a few minutes the anthers hang free on slender filaments. This allows the morning breezes to swing

The male and female flower parts of grasses are borne on the flowering spikes. There are no colorful blooms. The tiny "bottle-brushes" are the stigmas or female flower parts, while the male organs or anthers are elongate bodies with grooves down their centers.

them about and in so doing the pollen is sifted out and carried away. If, however, there is no wind and the grass remains still, the pollen does not sift out of the anthers. It is obvious that if the pollen sifted out in still air it would simply fall to the ground and be wasted.

While most grasses liberate their pollen early in the morning, there are some kinds that do so later in the day. A few kinds scatter their pollen twice a day. In any case, this wind-blown pollen is not liberated during damp weather, the most favorable conditions being warm, dry weather with dew and morning breezes.

It is a strange fact that evolution sometimes reverses itself and goes backward. The remote ancestors of the pines were wind-pollinated just as they are today. They have not changed. On the other hand, almost all of the great tribe of flowering plants began to depend on insects for pollination soon after these creatures arrived upon the world scene. Strangely, a number of these flowering plants "back-slid," losing their insect-attracting petals and becoming wind-pollinated again. Examples of these back-sliding plants are the grasses and ragweeds. It is probable that this return to ancestral wind pollination is an adaptation to help them secure proper pollen transfer. Imagine, if you can, the enormous number of bees that would be needed to pollinate the grasses on the thousands of square miles of our western plains. There are just not that many bees.

A large number of the plants that depend on wind for polli-nation have developed special adaptations. For example, in order for air-borne pollen to reach the stigmas of the female flowers there must be few obstructions. If a tree was covered with dense foliage at the time the pollen was liberated, most of it would adhere to the leaves. This would serve no useful pur-pose. Nature, as usual, has taken care of this problem. There is a pond where I often take field trips. Growing around this pond are many alders which always put forth their catkins or tassels

64

and shed their abundant pollen in winter. For several years I failed to realize the significance of this habit. The truth, of course, is that the alders, like a number of other trees, shed their precious pollen before there are leaves to obstruct it. This habit is found in many other wind-pollinated trees, including ash and elm. In the case of oaks and some other trees the pendant catkins emerge and shed their pollen just as the young leaves are beginning to unfold. Thus pollination is completed before the leaves have expanded enough to interfere with the free passage of the pollen.

The pollen of wind-pollinated plants has special characteristics that fit it for travel by air. The individual grains are usually small and do not usually stick together in clumps as do pollen grains regularly carried by insects and birds. One can easily understand that pollen intended to be transported by animals must be somewhat sticky so it will adhere to legs or beaks. Wind pollen is powdery like flour. Pine pollen is especially interesting since each grain has two attached air bladders that give it great buoyancy. That is the reason that it is carried so far by winds.

One of the chief differences between wind- and insect-pollinated flowers is in the amount of pollen produced. A flower whose pollen is carried by insects or birds can afford to be quite economical in pollen production since these animals are quite dependable carriers. Plants that must depend on the vagaries of winds, on the other hand, must produce great quantities of pollen if any of it is going to lodge by chance on the stigmas of other flowers of the proper kind. Most wind-blown pollen, naturally, ends up on the ground or other inhospitable places. Here it dies, of course, since the life of most pollen is usually but a few hours. It is probable that each alder catkin produces about two million pollen grains! Now in order to reduce the chances of pollen falling upon the stigmas of female flowers on the same tree, the flowers have an interesting arrangement that ensures the more desirable cross-pollination instead of self-pollination. If you examine an alder twig from which the catkins are suspended you will see that there is a tiny cone protruding up *above* the catkins. This cone is the female flower, and it is here that the pollen must alight if fertilization is to occur. When wind causes the suspended catkins to sway about, little clouds of yellow pollen are carried away. But this pollen does not usually float directly upward and so does not lodge upon the stigmas of the same tree. The chances are good that the grains will float away and that at least some of them will find lodging places on the stigmas of other alder trees nearby, thus bringing about cross-pollination. This pollen is very light in weight and is apt to be carried quite a distance. It has been estimated that one of these grains falls through the air at the rate of about an inch a second. At this rate it would take a grain two minutes to fall ten feet. Now if a pollen grain were being carried along by a wind blowing ten miles per hour, it would float for about a third of a mile before it finally settled to the ground. This is assuming that it did not lodge on an alder stigma or some object along the way. As we said before, the pollen of these small trees is shed in winter before they are leafed out, so there are no leaves to interfere with pollen movement.

There is another characteristic of wind-pollinated plants that has not been mentioned yet, but one which is probably quite important. Most of these plants have their stigmas especially modified for catching "flying" pollen. Alder has filamentous or hairy stigmas, while those of grasses look somewhat like tiny bottle brushes. Practically all these plants have their stigmas modified in some similar way to increase their chances of capturing drifting pollen.

We saw above how the flowers of alder were arranged so as to reduce the chances of self-pollination. Some other trees have made self-pollination impossible. These are ones such as in the cottonwood and willow families that have male and female flowers borne on separate trees. In other words, there are male

These male oak catkins shed their pollen before their leaves are out, making it easier for flying pollen to reach other trees.

trees and female trees. Ginkgoes have the same arrangement. In all of these the flowers on the male trees have only stamens and those on the female trees have only stigmas. Thus, only cross-pollination or pollination between *separate* trees is possible. The trees belonging to the cottonwood family include cottonwood, aspen and poplar. Willows have gone a step beyond wind-pollination and have nectar glands which attract bees for their help in carrying pollen.

As you can see, flowers solve the problems of pollination in numerous remarkable ways, and the wind-pollinated kinds are no exception. Consider the case of the paper mulberry. The tiny

Some plants, like this jewel-weed, protect their pollen from rain by placing their blooms beneath leaves.

male flowers of this tree are arranged in spikes. Before the individual flowers open, the pollen-bearing stamens are coiled up inside. When conditions are right the flowers begin to open and the stamens, each with its pollen-filled anther, spring outward tossing their little loads of pollen into the air. The breeze then blows it away, perhaps to female paper mulberry flowers on other trees. Nature has seen to it that the male flowers toss their loads of pollen into the air only when conditions are just right. This usually occurs at sunrise when a dry wind is blowing. This dries the flower and causes a tension to develop inside. As the little blooms slowly open, the anthers snap out. In damp weather this tension within the flower does not develop and so they do not open. If they did open in damp weather, their pollen would be wet, and soggy pollen, of course, will not float through the air. The pellitories and some kinds of nettles also have mechanisms for tossing their pollen into the air, and we have already seen how grasses take the precaution of seeing that their pollen is liberated only in sunny weather. The box tree and ash also require dry winds to open their pollen containers.

We noted previously how the large pollen grains of pine are equipped with air-filled sacs or bladders that give them great buoyancy and enable them to float many miles on winds. Pine trees, like alders, have both male and female flowers on the same tree, but these are usually borne on separate branches. The male flowers or cones are small and grow in clusters, their color being yellow or sometimes red. When these cones are shedding their pollen in spring, only a slight jar is needed to send a shower of golden dust cascading down. Soon after the pollen is gone the male cones shrivel and drop off. The female or seed cones are also small at this stage and rather inconspicuous, far different from the mature seed-bearing structures that we know as pine cones. They are covered with small scales, which at the time of pollination do not fit tightly together, there being narrow slits between them. There are no feathery stigmas for ensnaring pollen as in other wind-pollinated plants. The grains of pollen simply fall in or near the open slits which at this time are filled with resinous fluid. Soon this fluid begins to dry and the enclosed pollen grains are drawn into the slits. These slits are called *micropyles,* meaning "little doors," which is quite appropriate since it is through these "doors" that the pollen grains enter. The micropyles then close. Within the cavities in the female cones the male and female cells slowly develop. What is quite unusual in the case of pine is that the entry of pollen into the cavities of the female cones, or pollination, occurs one spring, but it will be the following spring, a year later, before actual fertilization occurs. After this the tiny seed cone begins growth, which in some kinds, such as the sugar pines, may reach a length of two feet. Certainly, the pollination of pines is quite a complicated process, but we can be quite sure that it works or otherwise Nature would have abandoned it millions of years ago.

The May-apple hides its blooms beneath leaves for protection of its pollen.

CHAPTER 5

Golden Dust

$\mathcal{T}$he study of microscopic pollen grains is called *palynology* and while it might seem that such a subject would hold little of interest or value, a number of scientists have devoted their lives and written books regarding the study of these tiny particles of flower dust. Palynology is a relatively new science which was born in the Scandinavian countries, but there are now palynologists in many other lands including the United States.

Pollen is of interest to us for several reasons. Pollen floating in the air is the chief cause of hayfever, and pollen studies are also important to our knowledge of the plant life of the past. Plants have been producing pollen for many millions of years, so it is not surprising that pollen grains appear as fossils in ancient lake and pond sediments that are now turned to stone. These fossil pollen grains tell geologists much about the presence and distribution of trees and plants in prehistoric times. The tiny fossils are found, not only in hardened sediments, but in fossilized "flowers." This is especially true of the ancestors of the pines, ginkgoes and cycads. All three of these plant families can trace their ancestry far back into time. The ginkgoes or maidenhair trees originated about 225 million years ago, the pines 271 million years ago, and the cycads 100 million years ago. Some kinds of palm-like cycads still grow in Florida.

Fossil pollen grains also tell us much about ancient climates.

For example, fir tree pollen has been found along with the remains of cave men who lived about seventy thousand years ago. Therefore, the climate where these cave men lived was cool because fir trees flourish only in such climates. Pollen has also been found in the same formations as those containing the bones of the Neanderthal man who lived fifty thousand years ago in Europe. This pollen has been identified as that of date palms. Thus, we know that this low-browed ancestor of ours dwelled in a tropical or semi-tropical climate. The climate of Europe is now, of course, much too cool for date palms, proving that the climate has changed.

Pollens of many kinds are also abundant in peat beds which actually were once bogs where plant life, especially *Sphagnum* mosses, flourished thousands of years ago. Year after year these peat beds built up, layer by layer, until now they are many feet deep and consist of accumulated moss remains. Samples of pollen grains have been taken from different levels in these peat beds, and from them the kinds of plants that grew there have been determined. By this means it has been possible to tell what the climates were like in certain areas at the time when the great ice sheet came down into the northern United States during the Ice Age. The presence of fir and spruce pollen indicates that a particular area was close to the cold edge of the ice, but pine pollen tells us that the climate was warmer and that the ice was farther away. In some places pollen from hickory and oak trees has been found, indicating an even milder climate.

You, too, can make pollen studies of ancient pollen from peat beds where it once drifted down from plants and trees that lived several thousand years ago. Almost any garden store or greenhouse has bales of peat moss which has been harvested and shipped from peat beds in northern Europe. Place a cup of this plant material in a fruit jar and shake it up with some water. Let it stand for a few minutes and then skim off some of the material from the surface. If this is examined under a micro-

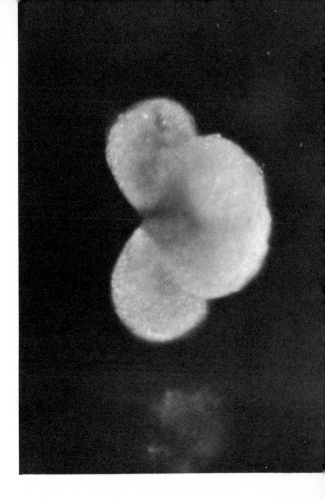

This pine pollen grain is prob-
ably over a thousand years
old. It is from a peat moss bed
in northern Europe.

scope you will find pollen grains of many kinds among the plant remains. The easiest pollen grains to identify will, of course, be those from pines and other conifers. (See the photograph above.) You cannot tell much, of course, about the age of pollen grains from commercial peat moss since you have no way of knowing from what depth it was obtained. When, however, palynologists are able to take samples very carefully from different levels in peat beds they find out some interesting things. At one location it was found, for example, that elm pollen was abundant in the lower levels but decreased in the higher levels. The same trend occurred in alder, birch and pine. Thus, the scientists knew that as time had passed, the kinds of trees growing in that vicinity had changed. At first there had been elm, but those trees had been successively replaced by alder, birch and then pine.

73

Studies of peat moss from Greenland are especially interesting because it contains considerable pine pollen, suggesting that pines may have flourished there long ago when the climate was much warmer. Other scientists believe that this pine pollen was carried by winds from the mainland of North America. These microscopic bits of flower dust offer many clues to the flora and climates of the past.

It has been pointed out that wind-pollinated plants must produce enormous quantities of pollen to compensate for the small chance of its alighting upon a female flower of the proper kind. In certain pines one male cluster of "catkins" sheds more than twenty-two million pollen grains. Oaks are less prolific since the average oak "flower" produces only about fifty thousand grains. The male flower of the common garden sorrel is probably the champion pollen producer, each one liberating nearly four hundred million pollen grains! It has been estimated that 75,000 *tons* of pollen are produced by the spruce forests of Sweden each summer! No estimates have been made of the total pollen output of pines in the United States, but the amount is certainly tremendous. As a general rule, wind-pollinated plants that grow far apart produce more pollen. For example, plants growing 100 inches apart produce about ten thousand times more pollen than those growing only an inch apart.

The fact that all pollen grains are very small is of great advantage, especially in transportation by winds. A tiny object will float in air while a larger and heavier object will not. If you drop a pollen grain from a tall building it will drift away on the breeze, but if you drop an orange from the same height it will spatter against the pavement. Gravity actually has little effect on an object as tiny as a pollen grain. Due to their minute sizes, pollen grains floating in the air are almost as weightless as a space capsule in orbit around the earth. Samples of air-borne pollen have been collected in the middle of the Atlantic Ocean. Included among these sea-going pollen grains were those from birch, pine, oak, willow and grasses. Pine pollen has also been found on the Greenland icecap where it had drifted from Labrador 400 miles away.

Some pollen grains are quite large, relatively speaking. Pumpkin pollen grains, for example, are about 200 microns in diameter. It would, thus, require only about 125 pumpkin pollen grains laid side by side to make an inch. These grains cannot float in air but are sticky and must depend upon insects for transportation. Air-borne pollen grains are much smaller than those of pumpkin. Alder pollen, for example, is only about 30 microns in diameter. Some pollen is even smaller, that of forget-me-not measuring only four-and-a-half microns. The best floaters are those between 17 and 58 microns. Pine pollen, which floats long distances in wind, measures about 50 microns. Along with that of other conifers such as spruce and fir, pine pollen has air-filled bladders or "wings" which give it great buoyancy.

The study of this air-borne pollen is especially important to those people who are so unfortunate as to suffer from hayfever. It is estimated that there are about three million hayfever suf-

Pine pollen, which may be carried hundreds of miles by winds, is very buoyant due to two air-filled bladders on each grain. Some of the pine pollen in this photomicrograph are turned on edge.

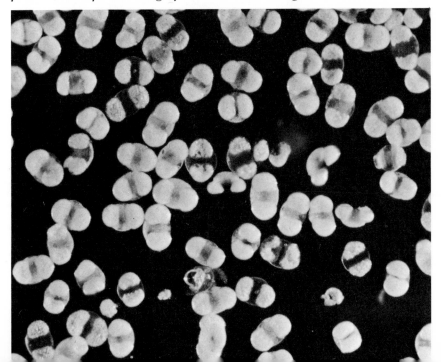

Goldenrod pollen is accused of causing hayfever. But gold-enrods are largely insect-pollinated and the real offenders are wind-pollinated flowers, such as ragweed, which bloom at the same time.

ferers in the United States alone. In the cases of some of these people, their sensitivity to certain kinds of pollen is so severe that they must move to pollen-free areas during certain seasons. A number of different plants produce pollen to which people are especially sensitive, and not all hayfever sufferers are sensitive to the same ones. Thus, one area may be better than another from a health standpoint. Most pollen allergies are also seasonal in nature because different plants and trees mature and shed their pollen at different times. As a general rule, plants with colorful flowers that attract insects to carry their pollen are not important in causing hayfever. People who are sensitive to elm, oak, poplar, birch and willow are affected in early spring since these trees shed their pollen before the leaves are out. One of the most important trees to the hayfever sufferer is the mountain cedar of Texas and New Mexico which spreads its objectionable pollen in the air during December.

Early summer is a time of suffering to many hayfever victims, due largely to the great number of grasses that mature and shed pollen at that time. These attacks are often called "rose colds" in the mistaken belief that they are caused by rose pollen. Roses, of course, are insect-pollinated so their pollen is not carried by wind. Probably the most important hayfever grass is timothy, a native of Europe, but grown in many parts of this country for hay.

Late summer, too, is hayfever time for many people, and they often attribute their suffering to goldenrod. The truth is that the goldenrods are insect-pollinated and, like roses, are usually innocent. The offending pollens in late summer come mostly from ragweeds which mature at the same time as goldenrod. About half of the hayfever in this country is caused by the various species or kinds of ragweed. Other important hayfever pollens at this season are from wormwoods, sagebrushes, Russian thistle or tumbleweed, and cocklebur.

It has been found that the heating and cooling of the earth's atmosphere causes floating pollen to rise and fall. During warm days the air rises, carrying pollen with it, to the relief of hayfever sufferers. When the air cools, the air—and suspended pollen—sinks. Rain, of course, washes the atmosphere free of all dust and pollen.

So far we have said very little about the microscopic structure of these bits of flower dust. If you will collect a number of different kinds from various flowers such as pine, dandelion, ragweed, sunflower, sundew or birch, and examine them in a water suspension under a microscope, you will find their forms almost as varied as those of snowflakes. There are spheres, stars, and triangles. Some kinds such as those from azalea blooms look like four tiny spheres attached together. Sunflower pollen

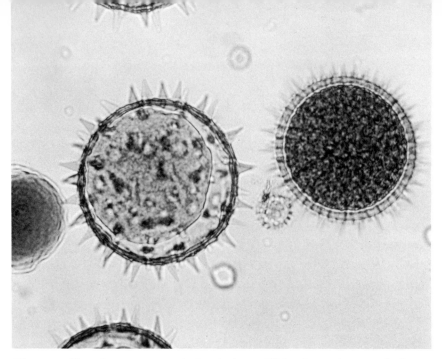

Flower pollens have great variation in form. This photomicrograph shows how they look under a microscope.

grains look like tiny, many-pointed stars. It is this varied structure that enables palynologists to identify them.

If you are interested, you can also study the germination of pollen grains. When pollen arrives—either via insects or wind—upon the flower stigma each grain sends a pollen tube down through the pistil toward the ovary where fertilization occurs. By using the proper techniques you can actually see these pollen grains sending out their tubes under a microscope. All that is needed is the placing of a tiny bit of pollen in a sugar solution on a microscope slide and keeping it warm for two or three hours. Most kinds of pollen will produce tubes in sugar solutions of from 2 to 50 per cent concentration in water. Some kinds are rather specific in their requirements, so you may have to do some experimenting. Fresh pollen works best. Try honeysuckle in 20 per cent sugar solution, sweet pea in 10 per cent, and petunia in 25 per cent.

No discussion of pollen would be complete without mentioning its value to honeybees. To these industrious insects pollen is the staff of life. It is collected by bees, as we have seen, and carried back to the hive where it is stored in the wax cells as "bee bread," and used as food for young bees. Pollen is a very nutritious food, furnishing large amounts of fat, proteins, and vitamins. Adult bees can get along with a diet of nectar alone, but the young developing bees must have these other dietary ingredients. It has been determined that about a pound of pollen is required to rear 3,000 bees. The average load of pollen carried by a worker bee during a foraging trip weighs about 12 milligrams (a milligram is one thousandth of a gram). From this it can be calculated that 37,735 trips are needed to carry a pound of pollen back to the hive. On each of these trips a bee must usually visit many flowers to obtain a full load. Some kinds of flowers require more visits than others, depending on the pollen yield. In the case of nasturtiums, a bee must collect the pollen from more than a hundred blooms to make a load. Each day while weather is fine the average worker bee goes on about fifty

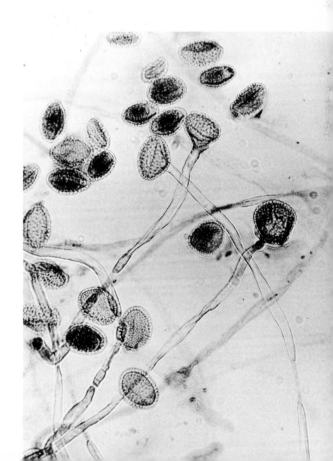

When flower pollen alights or is deposited upon a flower's stigma, each grain sends out a pollen tube that grows down into the ovary, bringing about fertilization and seed growth.

This cut-away view of a pitcher plant bloom shows how it protects its precious pollen. The greatly enlarged stigma forms a shield. The tiny projection at the top is the sensitive portion where pollen must be deposited to assure pollination.

of these pollen harvesting trips. Is it any wonder, then, that the life of a worker during summer is only five weeks? At this season the bees literally work themselves to death obtaining sufficient pollen and nectar to keep the hive supplied.

Considering how important pollen is to plants, it is not at all surprising to find that many flowers are provided with quite elaborate precautions to protect it. Among the robbers who come seeking nectar are the ants that drink their fill and crawl away.

80

Since they are not winged and cannot go readily from one plant to another, they are of little help in pollination. But many flowers are able to foil these thieves. The lower lip of the snapdragon, for example, is held tightly closed and can only be opened by a heavier insect such as a bumblebee. In other cases—the spiderworts, for instance—the pollen is protected by a tangle of fine filaments surrounding the stamens which makes it difficult for ants to rob them. Other flowers have their lines of defense in sticky stems which prevent crawling insects from reaching them. Good examples of this are found among the catchflys such as the fire pink. The small blooms of the toadflax hide their nectar in long slender spurs where only a long-tongued insect such as a bee can reach it. Flowers must also protect their precious pollen from rain, and they employ a number of different methods of doing this. In the case of the huckleberry the blooms are shaped like tiny bells that hang down so that rain cannot enter them.

This photograph of huckleberry blooms was taken in the rain. Note how the drops of water are suspended from the bell-shaped flowers. The pollen inside is thus protected from moisture.

This toadflax bloom foils ant robbers in two ways.
Only a heavy insect, such as a bee, can press down
the lower petal and enter the flower, and the nectar
is hidden far down in the spur beyond reach of most
crawling insects.

The fire pink protects its pollen from ant thieves by
sticky hairs on its stem.

The open, vase-like flower of the jack-in-the-pulpit is provided with a hood that extends out over the top. On the other hand, some flowers hold their "faces" up to the sun on clear days, but droop them during wet weather.

Many flowers, as we have seen, are dependent upon bees to carry their pollen from flower to flower and bring about cross-pollination. Bees do this, of course, more or less accidentally while gathering pollen and nectar for their own needs. Still, it is an important service to the flowers, and most flowers cannot get along without this help. Thus, it is indeed strange to find that there are some flowers whose pollen and nectar are actually poisonous to bees. The pollen of the California buckeye, for example, is poisonous to the queen bee, since it appears to destroy her egg-laying ability. Other plants poisonous to honeybees are black nightshade, death camas, dodder, leatherwood, locoweed, mountain laurel and yellow jessamine.

The orchids are, of course, the aristocrats of the flower tribe, so it is not surprising that some of them have gone so far as to provide their insect helpers with special "flower dust" that serves as food but which is actually not pollen at all. Orchids of the genus *Eleanthus* and *Polystachya* produce masses of this "flower dust" which collects in cups on the lower petals or "lips." This flour-like material is highly nutritious, containing starch, sugar, oil and proteins, and it serves as food for insects just as does pollen. In this way these orchids conserve their pollen for the important function of pollination. One wonders why other flowers have not "thought of" this idea.

At dusk the leaves of mimosa fold up for the night, but the pale tinted stamens are still exposed for dusk-loving insects.

CHAPTER 6

A Time to Bloom

One spring a number of years ago I wished to obtain photographs of lady's-slipper orchids which usually bloomed during the first week of May. That particular spring, however, had been unusually dry and much of the vegetation was parched and shriveled. Would the orchids bloom on schedule? It certainly seemed doubtful in view of the unusual weather conditions. With the arrival of May, though, I visited the deep woods where the lady's-slippers usually bloomed and, sure enough, there they were in full flower, each stalk holding up its delicately tinted blossom. Nature had not failed to bring them into bloom at the appointed date. What miracle of timing had Nature used? How did the orchids, hidden beneath the dark earth, know when the time was ripe for their debuts?

What I had forgotten was that in nature there is a time and a season for all things and each act, such as blooming and fruiting, usually occurs at an appointed time. The incident of the orchids demonstrates one of the basic laws of flowering. Most kinds of flowers have a time of their own, and there is little we can do to change it, unless we grow the flowers under artificial conditions and have control over the natural forces that affect them. In Jamaica, there is a certain kind of bamboo that grows for thirty-two years, then blooms and dies. But even when this plant is grown in other lands it still follows its 32-year sequence of

Flowers bloom when their time arrives. Snowdrops often flower while snow is still on the ground.

growth and blooming. Certain animals, too, are known to possess these living calendars. We have only to recall the precise emergence schedules of the 17-year cicadas that dwell beneath the earth for seventeen years and then, as if alerted by some unseen force, crawl forth to sing and mate and begin a new generation.

People have always known that most plants come into flower at definite seasons of the year. Even the cave man, perhaps, was conscious of the fact that certain plants bloomed and produced edible fruit at special times. No doubt he realized that blackberries could be gathered during a certain phase of the moon in spring. Possibly he called this the Blackberry Moon—who knows? But the cave man neither knew nor cared about the reasons behind the seasonal nature of blooming and fruiting. It was sufficient to him to know when wild fruits and edible herbs could be harvested.

The modern biologist, however, is not satisfied to know merely that a thing occurs; with his inquiring mind, he must know the reasons why. Biologists do not yet know all the answers to the intriguing questions concerning these built-in flower clocks and calendars, but many remarkable things have recently been found out about them.

We usually accept the fact that flowers bloom at their proper seasons without giving it much thought. Violets bloom in the spring because that is when violets bloom. But when the biologists began poking their inquisitive noses into the private lives of flowers they came up, as usual, with some theories as to the basic causes of flowering. Not too long ago it was believed that the flowering process was triggered by the accumulation of foods within the plant. This seemed logical and is true up to a certain point, but it did not explain everything. Why is it that even though a plant has accumulated an adequate food supply it still does not bloom until its proper season arrives?

Many flowers follow the sun. These prairie Coreopsis were photographed in early morning when each one had its face turned toward the rising sun.

It remained for two scientists named W. W. Gardner and H. A. Allard to find the answer to this question. They grew some plants in greenhouses that could be darkened to simulate short days and other plants in greenhouses that had electric lights turned on to simulate long days. They discovered that there are flowers that bloom only when the days are short, as in spring and autumn when the days are less than twelve hours long. These they called *short-day* plants. Another class of plants, they discovered, blooms only when the days are long, as in mid-summer. They called these *long-day* plants. Such plants will bloom even when grown under continuous light. But the scientists found that there was yet a third class of plants that would bloom during either short or long days, so they named them *day-neutral* plants. Practically all the economically important flowering plants have been classified as to the group to which they belong. For example, the following are known to be short-day plants: chrysanthemum, cocklebur, dogwood, cosmos, goldenrod, orchid, poinsettia, ragweed, and aster. Long-day plants include red clover, dill, althea, larkspur, radish, sedum, spinach, and sugarbeet. The blooming of many common plants seems not to be affected much by day length and these, as we have said, are called day-neutral plants. A few examples are string beans, buckwheat, cotton, cucumber, geranium, pansy, snapdragon, and tomato. As one might expect, there are a number of flowers that bloom both in spring and and in autumn since the days are of about equal length during these seasons. Some kinds of daisies, milkweeds and goldenrods, for example, appear in fields in spring or summer, while other kinds bloom in the fall.

When short-day plants are grown under long-day conditions they usually continue to grow but never bloom. On the other hand, some garden plants, like tomatoes, may be injured or killed when subjected to such long days. Actually, tomatoes are day-neutral plants whose flowering depends mostly upon the number of nodes or "joints" in the stem. Most varieties of tomatoes do not produce flower buds until about thirteen nodes have been formed. Some long-day plants, such as rock garden sedums, may grow for many years without ever flowering when kept under short-day conditions. It is interesting to note, too, that when such light-starved plants are given additional hours of light they quickly form blooms. In our temperate region, days range in length from about fifteen hours in summer to about nine hours in mid-winter.

Thus, it has been known for a long while that day-length controlled the flowering dates of many plants. Scientists gave it a name, *photoperiodism,* referring to the length of time plants are exposed to sunlight. This was a theory that could be tested by experiments. Many scientists became interested in these day-length experiments and considerable research was carried out in a search for the basic causes. They grew many kinds of plants in greenhouses where the day-lengths could be artificially controlled. In this way they found out a lot of interesting things, but they were still not satisfied and continued to experiment with flowering plants.

One of their favorite experimental plants was the common cocklebur, a plant that is very sensitive to light conditions. Cockleburs will bloom only when they receive fifteen hours or less of sunlight. Thus, in Canada where summer days are very long these weeds continue to grow, but do not usually bloom until too late for them to form seeds. Farther south, however, in their normal habitat, cockleburs bloom much earlier.

Biologists, using these light-sensitive cockleburs, made another experiment. They exposed different plants to different periods of daylight and then grafted them together. It was found that when a cocklebur that had been grown under eighteen hours of light, and which normally would not bloom, was grafted onto one grown under only twelve hours of light, which would bloom, they both produced flowers. What did this experiment prove? It proved that whatever it was that controlled blooming was transferred from one plant to the other through the graft. The scientists thus realized that there was some chemical regulator being produced by the short-day cocklebur. They named this unknown substance *florigen* because it apparently "generated" or stimulated flowering.

This brings us to the next step in solving the mystery of blooming. As evidence we might cite *"The Case of the Poinsettias that Bloomed Too Late."* In a certain commercial greenhouse the large stock of poinsettias bloomed too late for the Christmas season. As a result, the greenhouse lost a considerable amount of money. After a good deal of investigation it was finally discovered that the night watchman used a very powerful flashlight and, in his rounds of the greenhouse each night, he swept its beam about over the growing poinsettias. This relatively small amount of light was apparently sufficient to delay flowering. Research done at the Ohio Agricultural Experiment Station has shown that if greenhouses where poinsettias are growing have the electric lights turned on for one hour during the middle of each night from September 22 to October 10, the plants begin flowering on December 20. They normally begin blooming on about December 10; thus, their blooming is delayed ten days which more nearly coincides with the Christmas season. Poinsettias are short-day plants that bloom in late autumn or early winter when the days are short. We know now that such plants as poinsettias and chrysanthemums should actually be spoken of as *long-night* plants rather than *short-day* plants because it is the length of the *nights* rather than the length of the days that is important. This may sound like two ways of saying the same thing, but there is a difference, as we shall see. It is the chemical reactions that go on in plants during the hours of darkness that actually determine their time of blooming. Just how this works is quite complicated and, as yet, not fully understood by scientists.

It has been found that there is, in plants, a certain colored material or pigment called *phytochrome*. It is present in very

The blooms of the false dragonhead flower begin opening at the base of the spike and each day open progressively up the stalk until all have opened and been pollinated. The pollinated flowers then wither and drop off.

minute amounts and occurs in two forms designated as P_{660} and P_{735}. When P_{660} is activated by exposure to red light it is changed into P_{735}. In living plants the phytochrome 660 (P_{660}) is slowly converted into phytochrome 735 (P_{735}) in the presence of sunlight which, of course, contains red light rays. Now when darkness comes the P_{735} slowly changes back into P_{660} and the rate at which this change occurs is like a clock that "tells" the plant how long the night is.

Let us now see how this phytochrome clock affects the time of blooming. We have already seen how brief periods of light at night caused poinsettias to delay blooming. This apparently occurred because a short period of light affected these chemical regulators so that the plant responded as if the night were short. These phytochromes or chemical "clocks" are believed to control many plant and flower functions including leaf growth, seed

91

Oxalis flowers open their petals at 8 or 9 o'clock in the morning on sunny days and wait for bees and other day-flying insects.

germination, and red coloration of apples, as well as the time of blooming. When plants such as petunias are given short light exposures during long winter nights they are stimulated into blooming even though they may be short-night plants that normally bloom in mid-summer.

Now, you might ask, "How many long nights must a plant that has been on a short night schedule have to begin flowering?" There is a great difference in plant sensitivity in this respect. Our old friend the cocklebur begins forming buds after being placed in a long-night greenhouse for only one day! Chrysanthe-

With the coming of dusk oxalis blooms close up for the night. This protects them from dew. Most flowers unfold at definite times of the day.

mums, which are long-night plants, need from eight to thirty long nights to begin blooming after having been grown under short-night conditions.

The time of flowering is very important to many plants and often is the thing that limits their geographic range. We have seen that the long summer days, or rather the short summer nights, in Canada cause cockleburs to bloom only very late in the summer. Actually, these plants bloom so late at that latitude that, under field conditions, they are killed by frost before their seeds can mature. The same thing is true of ragweed and many other plants. On the other hand, a plant such as spinach does not produce flowers in tropical lands because, to produce flowers, it needs at least two weeks of ten-hour nights. Nights are never that short in the Tropics.

These hours-of-darkness requirements of plants are very important to everyone who grows flowers. People often bring plants or their seeds back from an extended trip and plant them, fully expecting eventually to see pretty flowers like the ones they saw on their trip. In many instances these "foreign" plants thrive but never bloom, the answer probably being that the day length— or night length—in their new home is not conducive to flowering. This is especially true of plants that are moved either northward or southward from their native regions. Many plants, too, are very sensitive to the *amount* and *kind* of light they receive. Some plants, like sunflowers, grow best in exposed conditions where they receive the full sun. Other plants such as woods violets thrive best in deep shade where there is only a hundredth as much light. Deep shade plants cannot thrive in full sunshine. Thus, we see that each flower has its own special light requirement. You would not expect to find violets in a desert nor cacti in a deep forest. There is also, of course, the matter of moisture.

Flowers not only have seasons and other requirements for blooming; most of them also have rather definite times of the day when they unfold their petals. Some flowers unfold but once, then shrivel and die. In other cases flowers close and reopen several days in succession. In some extreme cases the petals may unfold again and again for as many as twelve days. In many instances, of course, flowers open and remain so until fertilization occurs. Poppies and portulacas have a brief blooming period, but others, like orchids, may remain in bloom for many weeks. Naturally, the longer a flower remains open the better are its chances of pollination. Some flowers "put all their eggs in one basket" and produce but a single bloom. In others, such as the spiderworts (*Tradescantia*), fresh blooms are pro-

94

duced each morning. The number of days that individual blooms remain fresh is rather precise, and it may be interesting to mention a few examples. They are as follows:

Two-day flowers:	Geranium, poppy, ironweed, bouncing bet, carnation and willow herb
Three-day flowers:	Honeysuckle, cinquefoil (five-finger), bedstraw, and agrimony
Four-day flowers:	Campion, pearlwort, sedum and wild hyacinth
Five-day flowers:	Fritillaria, centuary, and flax
Six-day flowers:	Digitalis, day lily (some kinds) and oxalis
Seven-day flowers:	Buttercup, and others
Eight-day flowers:	Winter aconite, hepatica, parnassia and saxifrage
Ten-day flowers:	Cyclamen, and others
Thirty-day flowers:	Cattleya and other orchids

Most of the blooms that last longer than about two weeks are orchids of various kinds.

The opening and closing of flowers is Nature's means of protecting the flowers' pollen supplies. One of the first botanists to make careful observations of the rather definite hours of flower opening and closing was Carolus Linnaeus. He once planted many kinds of flowers carefully selected for their times of blooming in his garden in Upsala, Sweden. These flowers were so arranged that one could tell time by noting which flowers were open. He called this a Flower Clock, and it was possible to tell time quite accurately by it. Of course, this "clock" had no minute hands and it was possible to tell only the hours. Linnaeus' flower clock had no practical use, but it did prove that blooms open at precise times of the day. A few common flowers have been timed as to their times of opening and closing. Four-o'clocks open at about four o'clock in the afternoon. *Tradescantia*

The birth of a flower. At dusk the white bloom of Datura *or angel-trumpet begins to unfold. (See next photograph.)*

opens between 5 and 6 A.M. and closes in mid-afternoon. Oxalis is a late sleeper, unfolding its petals between 8 and 9 A.M. and closing them in late afternoon. *Hibiscus* blooms open about the same time but close sooner. *Portulaca* opens about 9 A.M. and remains so until dusk. *Datura* is a night bloomer that unwinds its snowy flowers at dusk and folds them at sunrise. The same thing is true of *cleome*. The queen-of-the-night cactus expands its remarkable blossoms late at night and few people ever have the privilege of seeing them.

Anyone can make observations on the opening and closing times of flowers. The times given above may not, of course, be the same for the flowers in your own locality. As one travels north or south the sequences of blooming will vary.

It is common knowledge that temperatures, also, affect plant growth and blooming. Tropical plants need higher temperatures than plants of temperate climes, but one can encounter familiar

Within a few minutes the flower is fully expanded and ready to attract night-flying moths for pollination. The bloom also exhales a heavy perfume. (See next photograph.)

By dawn the Datura bloom, having fulfilled its function, wilts and dies.

northern plants on high mountains in the Tropics. This occurs because high mountain temperatures even in the Tropics are cool.

Plants are usually well adapted to their native regions. I recall a night in early June when heavy snow began falling at a ranch near the Teton Mountains in Wyoming. With the snow came a sharp fall in temperature to two degrees below freezing. The hillsides at the time were colorful with alpine flowers, but, strangely, when the sun came out next morning the snow melted and the flowers were as fresh as ever. These alpine flowers are well adapted to the severe climate in which they live. Flowers of milder climates would certainly have been killed.

Many plants and flowers, as we have seen, are very sensitive to differences in climates and will thrive only in the climate to which they are adapted. This is quite graphically illustrated in the case of high mountain flora. If we climb the slopes of a mountain in the Rockies we find that as we go upward the kinds of flowers change. At the foot of the mountain the meadows may be colorful with red gilia and blue lupine. A couple of thousand feet higher the gilias are gone, while some of the lupines are still in bloom. Here, among small groves of quaking aspen, also grow wild geraniums and roses. Another arduous climb brings us up to the realm of the true alpine flowers that thrive above 8,000 feet. Here the slopes are golden with balsam-root sunflowers and in the deep, wooded glens grow columbines, Indian paintbrushes, elephant's-heads, and glacier lilies. In moist places we may find rare orchids.

As we continue our ascent up the mountain, we find that at about 11,000 feet we have left some flowers behind and encountered new ones. This is a region of stunted trees, often twisted into strange shapes by the inhospitable climate. Strangely, it is also the home of many interesting flowers. Here in protected places grow pyrolas, louseworts, and shooting stars. During the brief alpine summer they bloom and add their touches of color.

If we are rugged individuals and physically able, we may continue our climb until we have left the last stunted tree behind. We are now above the "timber line" in an area where the sparce vegetation finds shelter only between the rocks. Even during summer, snow is usually found in sheltered ravines on the north slopes. Winds blow almost continually, and each night the temperature drops to near the freezing point. It will probably surprise you to find that, even in these surroundings, numerous flowers thrive. Here grow gold flowers, avens, yellow saxifrages, blue skunk flowers and patches of alpine sandworts. Many of these alpine flowers are quite fragrant.

Biologists have divided these elevations up into "life zones," and each one has its own characteristic flora. These "life zones" are especially evident in the high mountains of the West, but you can also observe how vegetation changes with changes in elevation in the Great Smoky Mountains and in other high areas. If you travel northward across the United States you will encounter similar successive "life zones." In other words, traveling northward has about the same effect as climbing upward. When you have climbed to the top of a high mountain in the United States you are actually in the same "life zone" as you would be at sea level in northern Canada. Another way of saying it is that at the top of one of our higher mountains you are actually in an "arctic" region. Not only do flower types change with changes in elevation and distance northward, but their times of blooming also change. The higher one climbs, or travels northward, the later in the season are plants in flower.

In bygone days housewives often placed dried rose petals in special containers called "rose jars." The fragrances of summer blooms could thus be preserved all year. Many of these old rose jars are still in existence.

CHAPTER 7

Flower Perfumes

It is a little difficult to say whether people first became interested in flowers for their pretty colors or for their perfumes. When Cleopatra sailed down the Nile to meet Mark Antony it is said that the purple sails of her barge were scented with perfumes. There is in existence a bill from Houbigant, Paris perfumers, to Napoleon for perfumed gloves and other toilet articles. It is dated May 17, 1815, just a month before Napoleon's defeat at Waterloo.

Certainly, the art of perfumery is an ancient craft and the pleasant odors of flowers have enriched men's lives down the centuries. A thing is doubly pleasant if it appeals to more than one of our five senses, and flowers certainly fit in this category. They appeal to our sense of sight, of course, by their bright colors and symmetry of form. But to our sense of smell there is nothing equal to the fragrance of flowers. These scents range from the delicate odors of violets blooming in the cool of the forest to the heavy pungent smell of bergamot and *Datura*.

Scientists have often made attempts at classifying odors, but odors are elusive things comparable only to the delicate hues of a rainbow after a summer shower. Flower perfumes defy accurate description. How would you describe the smell of a rose to a person who had never even seen a rose?

In southern France where most of the world's perfume indus-

101

try is centered there are people who spend their lives sniffing vintage perfumes. These people are known in the perfume industry as "noses" and they are experts in the art of perfumery, yet to all of us various flowers have distinctive smells and we can distinguish between many common kinds. Still our noses can be fooled. Sometime have a friend show you a flower, then close your eyes and have him hold another kind of flower to your nose. This will usually completely confuse your sense of smell. Imagination often has much to do with odors. I once tried this out on a biology class. I opened a glass jar on the lecture table, saying that it contained an extract from skunk glands. I then asked the students to hold up their hands when they smelled the scent. After a minute or so a number of hands were raised in various parts of the room. Actually, the jar contained only water!

The substances that impart their fragrances to flowers are called essential oils, but they are not really oils at all. True oils do not evaporate if left exposed to the air, whereas essential oils gradually pass off into the air and disappear. These substances are also called "flower oils" or essences and they do have an oily feel somewhat resembling that of a true oil such as coconut oil or lubricating oil.

The manufacture of most of the world's perfumes is centered in southern France at the city of Grasse, a small town having a population of about 15,000. It is an old city beautifully situated in the hills a few miles above Cannes and surrounded by fields of flowers and rose gardens. Here, beside the blue Mediterranean, are grown the flowers that perfume the world. From the factories of Grasse come the essences or flower oils that are blended into perfumes of endless variety. The extraction of these essences is perhaps the most interesting step in the manufacturing process. The first step, of course, is the growing and harvesting of the flowers from which the basic essences are obtained. The soil of this region of sunny France seems especially adapted to flower culture on a large scale. Here grow jasmine, rose, violet,

102

The delicate perfume of violets has always been held in esteem. Hundreds of tons of violets are harvested each summer in southern France.

mimosa and carnation, as well as orange blossoms. Most of these blooms must be harvested at certain times of the day. For instance, jasmine must be harvested before sunrise, while carnations need the heat of the sun to produce their best perfume. It is a little difficult for us to imagine the almost fantastic quantities of flowers that are used at Grasse in its role as flower essence capital of the world. During the last year for which figures are available, more than 2,000 tons of orange blossoms, 1,500 tons each of rose and jasmine, and 500 tons of violets were harvested.

Immediately after harvest these flowers are rushed to the processing plants where the essences are extracted by methods that have changed but little with the coming of modern times. There are four ways that these flower essences are extracted. The first is by placing the flowers or petals in presses and squeez-

The pungent perfume of gardenias is one of the perfumers' favorites.

ing out the fragrant oils. This method is used in obtaining oils from orange, lemon, and bergamot blossoms. The second method of essence extraction is that of steam distillation in which the flowers are heated with water in stills, the essential oils being driven off with the steam which condenses into droplets as it leaves the stills. The distillation of flower essences is an ancient craft that was first practiced in crude form nearly 7,000 years ago. In the third method the flowers are heated in vats of fat which absorbs the essence. The essence is then dissolved out of the fat by means of alcohol. This is called the maceration process. The fourth essence extraction method is the most interesting one of all and is the one much used at Grasse. It is called *enfleurage* and is as follows: Flower petals are plucked and rushed to the factories before they have had time to lose their fragrance. Here they are spread on layers of purified lard by hand. The lard absorbs the fragrance or essence and these petals are then removed and another layer of petals applied. This is repeated until the lard has absorbed all the essence it will hold, after which the essence or flower oil is extracted from the lard with alcohol or by freezing. The resulting concentrated scent is called an attar (or otto). The enfleurage process has been in use for centuries. About four tons of rose petals are required to produce a pound of attar.

The different methods of essence extraction often work better with one kind of flower than with another kind. The maceration method is used for cassia and violet, while enfluerage is used for jasmine, tuberose, orange blossom and jonquille.

These flower oils, essences, or attars, whichever you prefer to call them, are very expensive as you can well imagine, often costing as much as six hundred dollars a pound. They are the basic materials out of which most of the perfumes that you buy are made. As we shall see, it is usually a long step from the flowered fields of south France to the bottle of perfume in a department or drug store. In a few cases, however, the alcoholic flower extracts or, as the French say, *extraits aux fleurs* are sold as perfumes without further processing. And there are some flowers whose essences cannot be extracted. Examples are lilac and lily-of-the-valley. Perfumes having these scents are made artificially in the laboratory.

Expensive perfumes are usually compounded from a number of different ingredients, sometimes as many as fifteen or twenty. The blending of perfumes to achieve the finished product is a skilled craft and is usually surrounded by trade secrecy. Into the "brew," however, go many materials, some of which you would never suspect could add anything to the pleasant fragrance of flower oils. Some of these, in concentrated form, are very ill-smelling, indeed. It is often these vile smelling substances, though, that "hold" or "fix" the scents and keep them from passing off into the air in a short time. The ancient Egyptians were very skillful in the compounding of essences in such a manner that their fragrances lasted for a long while. When the Tomb of King Tutankhamen, who ruled in Egypt more than

3,000 years ago, was opened in 1922 a number of alabaster vases were found. Contained in these vases were the remains of perfumes and ointments that still held the aroma of flowers that had been plucked from forgotten fields thousands of years before.

These strange ingredients that hold flower fragrances often come from far places and their stories, too, add touches of romance to the science of perfume making. Into the perfumers' pots go such strange things as ambergris, musk from the musk deer, beaver and muskrat glands and civet from civet cats. Modern perfumes also contain various synthetic substances. Ambergris is a strange material that apparently comes from whales as partly digested squids. In a number of cases lumps of this ambergris have been washed up on beaches and the finders have profited by several thousand dollars since it brings a high price. A man in recent years found forty-four pounds of ambergris on the beach at New Bedford, Massachusetts, which he sold for $11,000. Civet comes from Ethiopia where tribesmen collect it from civet cats in captivity. From far Tibet come dried musk deer glands that are obtained at great risk because of the severe penalty for killing these animals. Beaver and muskrat glands are obtained by fur trappers. And so, from the far corners of the earth, from Tibet and Zanzibar and Ceylon, come the ingredients for this witch's brew that we call perfume.

The flowers of France contribute their fragrances, and the things that go into any particular perfume are closely guarded trade secrets, but it may be interesting to list those that go into one kind of perfume. They are as follows: tuberose absolute, rose otto, Canada snakeroot oil, bergamot oil, Cayenne linaloe oil, musk extract, dimethyl-hydroquinone, ethyl cinnamate, musk ambrette, coumarin, heliotropin, tincture of ginger, balsam Peru, orris oleo-resin, and benzoin. The above materials are blended in alcohol and the result is perfume! This will, perhaps, explain its high price.

The tuberose is not really a rose at all but a member of the Amaryllis family. Believed to be a native of either Mexico or the East Indies, its sweet perfume was once considered slightly intoxicating.

So far we have talked about the human uses of flower fragrances, but what about the flowers themselves? Why do they produce these sweet-smelling "oils"? In a previous chapter we saw how flowers use their colors as signboards to advertise their pollen and nectar to insects. Flowers have selfish reasons for producing perfumes or scents just as they have selfish reasons for producing nectar and excess pollen. They are another step in their advertising campaigns to lure insects for their help in carrying pollen. Some flowers are very fragrant while others have no scent at all as far as the human nose is concerned. Interestingly, too, the perfumes that are attractive to bees are usually the same ones that are also attractive to us, although the smelling organs of bees are from ten to a hundred times more sensitive than ours. Bees are able to detect some substances diluted down to one part in forty million parts of water! It has also been found that bees can detect small differences in very dilute mixtures of some substances. This great sensitivity of bees' organs of smell is, of course, very important to them in locating nectar sources. Bees' odor sense organs are located in their antennae or "feelers" and if their antennae are removed they lose their sense of smell. It has been found also that the actual sensory organs consist of tiny plates located on the last eight segments or joints of the antennae. There are about 2,400 of these plates on each of a worker bee's antennae. Drones have only 1,600 while the queen has 37,800. We may assume from this that the queen bee has a much keener sense of smell than either the workers or drones.

There are many flowers that emit vile odors, but it is to flies and beetles that such flowers appeal. For example, the large *Rafflesia* blooms of certain tropical lands are characterized by the odor of decaying flesh or carrion. This odor attracts flies which pollinate the flowers. The tremendous arum lily of Sumatra is another evil-smelling flower, but the insects that are attracted in this case are beetles. Many of us have seen starfish cactus in bloom since they are often grown in pots. These blooms are five to six inches in diameter and dark purple in color. They have a "perfume" that attracts flies. (This so-called "cactus" is actually a member of the milkweed family.) Another fly flower is the Dutchman's pipe that actually traps the flies inside until they have carried out the ritual of pollination.

I once climbed to the top of a high mountain in the Rockies, and there discovered a number of small blue flowers nestled among the rocks. When these flowers were smelled, however, it

108

One of the most fragrant flowers is the common nasturtium. The name itself refers to the attractive smell and means, literally, "to twist the nose." The perfume of the nasturtium is, of course, attractive to insects.

was found that their "perfume" resembled almost exactly that of a skunk. I found later that these flowers belong to the phlox family and are called alpine skunk flowers. Probably these attractive flowers depend upon small beetles or flies for pollination. In that cold, high altitude there are few bees or butterflies, so the flowers that bloom there must have other helpers.

Beetles and flies have relatively poor eyesight, so the flowers that depend on them must use something besides bright colors, especially at long range. Thus, it is not surprising that fly and beetle flowers are not usually very colorful, being more often dark shades of purple, greenish or brown. They are sometimes marked with violet streaks or brown veins. There are exceptions, of course, such as the beetle-pollinated blooms of magnolia, water lilies and dogwood, which are white. Many beetle flowers find it necessary to hide their developing seeds deep within the tissues of the flower head. This is because beetles have strong jaws and like to feed on any exposed parts of the flower, sometimes destroying them.

Nature is usually economical and does not often waste her products. Thus, brightly colored day-blooming flowers that cater to bees and butterflies do not usually emit much perfume; this is reserved for the insects of the dusk and night that must seek their food without the aid of sight. Examples are honeysuckles and petunias which have little smell during the daylight hours. On the other hand, there are some flowers whose perfumes smell differently at different times of the day. There is also a relationship between flower size and perfume content, many small flowers such as those of mignonette and *Eleagnus* emitting strong scents which can be perceived at quite a distance.

The gay colors of flowers are used to advertise their wares, but perfumes, too, help flowers in their efforts to attract bees, butterflies and birds. Without the help of these creatures many plants could not produce the seeds so necessary for their perpetuation.

The honeysuckle's flower lures night-flying insects in two ways. It spreads its perfume in the dusk and its white petals guide insects to the nectar deep within its throat.

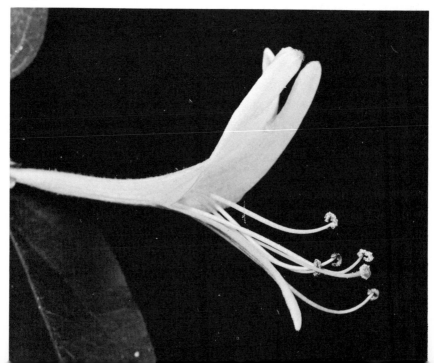

CHAPTER 8

Along the Pathways of Time

Someone once said that men are not only doers of deeds but also dreamers of dreams. Thus, it is not surprising that, down the centuries, flowers have often been adopted by men and nations as symbols of their destinies. This has been true since the days of Egypt when the lotus bloom was so esteemed that its form was adopted by the architects who designed the buildings with the lotus blossom capitals along the Nile. The snowy bloom of the water lotus was, of course, also regarded with supernatural awe in the land of ancient China. People have always loved and respected flowers because they somehow seemed to represent something pure and above the evils of the world. In ancient Rome the annual Festival of Floralia was celebrated on April 28 with games, dances and character plays. This was a tribute to Flora, goddess of flowers. An annual festival honoring chrysanthemums has been held in Japan for a thousand years. In our own country we have a somewhat similar event in California's annual Tournament of Roses.

To our ancestors flowers were often surrounded by symbolism and mystery, and their relationship to pollination and seed formation was unknown. They observed many wild flowers and cultivated some of them in their gardens. One of the most ancient of the cultivated flowers was the rose, and it has come down to us out of the dim mists of history. Just when man first began its cultivation no one knows. It is known that the rose was grown in ancient China nearly 5,000 years ago and that the art of rose culture spread westward to Greece and Rome and on to England and Europe. It is believed that roses were among the flowers grown in King Midas' garden, and the Island of Rhodes received its name from the Greek name for rose, or *rhodon.* When American colonists came to the New World they brought the rose with them. Thus, it has come to us out of the past. Certainly it is not the same as it was in the days when it flourished in China or in the monastery gardens of Medieval Europe. Down the ages gardeners have developed new varieties of almost endless kinds, from the miniature roses to the huge American Beauty, which, incidentally, originated in Europe. So roses have followed man in his wanderings, perhaps as symbols of the better way of life he hoped for and sought. Many a dreary settler's cabin on our own frontier was brightened by the red roses so carefully dug up and transported across the wilderness to new settings. To the settlers, especially the womenfolk, these rose bushes were reminders of the homes they had left behind.

Both the Greeks and the Romans dedicated the rose to the goddess of love as well as to the goddess of wine. But as time passed, beliefs in the ancient pagan gods faded away, and by the time of the crusades, from 1096 to 1270, roses were often emblazoned on the shields of knights merely as symbols. Soon after the crusades the Wars of the Roses were fought in England and lasted off and on for thirty years. These wars were between two rival royal Houses. These two Houses united at last, but not before many thousands of soldiers and noblemen had been slain. The House of Lancaster wore as its badge the red rose—the Rose Gule—and the House of York wore the white rose—the Rose Argent. (In heraldry *argent* means silver or white and *gule* means red.) The red rose had been brought back from France by the second son of Henry III, Edmund Crouchback, and became the symbol of the Lancastrians. Crouchback's brother,

For thousands of years roses have added touches of beauty and fragrance to men's lives. They appeared on the battle shields of crusaders, on heraldic coats-of-arms, and as symbols during the Wars of the Roses. This picture shows a wild rose.

Edward I, then chose the white rose as the badge of the opposing Yorkists. The Wars of the Roses were thus struggles for power between two related Houses. When the soldiers went into battle they wore caps bearing these rose emblems. There is a fable that when the wars were ended at last and the two Houses reunited a rose bush in a certain British monastery suddenly bore both red and white blooms. In any case, the rose symbol eventually emerged as the Tudor rose, the royal badge of England, consisting of a double rose with an outer row of red petals and an inner row of white petals. Thus are roses closely tied to British history and to heraldry.

In America roses have always been popular in gardens and greenhouses, and plant breeders have developed a vast array of beautiful varieties. The Cherokee rose was adopted by the State of Georgia as its State Flower, yet this particular rose is not native to America at all! It has an interesting history. Long ago this large white rose grew only in China. From there it was taken to Persia where it flourished in Persian gardens which were famed for their beauty. The roses were then transported to Spain by Arab Moslems and, eventually, brought to the Spanish settlements in Florida. Here they escaped from cultivation and people eventually forgot that they were not native to the New World. Thus, the Cherokee rose, now an American symbol, is a flower with a past whose ancestors came from far-off China. How they were transported from China to Persia we can only guess—perhaps by camel caravans across the vast stretches of southern Asia. Many of our most attractive flowers and flowering shrubs came from Persian gardens, for the flowers in these gardens were collected in far-off lands at great expense.

The common peach trees that bloom in American orchards are also natives of China that have come to us by way of Persia where they grew more than 2,000 years ago. It was once believed that the peach was native to Persia and even its botanical name, *Prunus persica*, reflects this assumption. As a matter of fact, peaches were once called "Persian apples."

Several of our other flowering fruit trees have followed this same path across the world to our orchards. One of these is the apricot which was brought to southeast Asia long before the time of Christ, and then was taken on to Greece by Alexander the Great during his conquests four hundred years B.C.

As you can see, the love of flowers is not new. Centuries before the dawn of the Christian era, the people of China,

Persia, Egypt and Greece practiced the cultivation of flowers for their beauty alone. Thus, we owe much to the ancient gardeners who gathered the wild ancestors of many of our most attractive flowers from far places and slowly developed them into more colorful and showy kinds. The use of flowered wallpaper originated in Egypt where walls were often decorated with flower garden scenes, and the designs of Persian rugs and carpets were—and still are—merely reproductions of formal gardens complete with water fountains. This is doubtless the origin of the flowered patterns of many modern carpets.

Flower gardens have slowly changed down the centuries. The custom of planting formal gardens apparently originated in Persia and spread to Egypt, Greece and on to Rome. These gardens were often planted in geometric patterns and bordered by flowers of contrasting color. In time, the typical English garden

The Cherokee rose is actually a native of China that was brought to the United States by early settlers.

came into vogue, consisting of green lawns bordered by flowering shrubs and flowers. This, of course, is the style now followed in America.

Long ago people were especially interested in the practical food or medicinal value of almost every new plant. Any new plant or flower was almost always tried out as a cure for various human ailments. Sometimes these potions helped, but more often they did not. Many of the old beliefs seem very strange and even foolish to us now in the light of scientific knowledge. For example, people once believed in what was called the Doctrine of Signatures. According to this belief all plants and flowers were placed on earth for human benefit and there was always some characteristic about every plant or herb that "told" what disease it would cure. As we all know, contact with a nettle plant causes a stinging sensation and, often, a skin rash. Thus, people believed that to cure any skin rash one should drink nettle tea. Similarly, it was long recommended that red rose petals be eaten to cure nose bleed. Some herbs were thought to be useful simply because of their shapes. Wood sorrel or oxalis was prescribed for heart diseases because of its heart-shaped leaves, and liverwort was used for liver ailments. We know now, of course, that there is no scientific basis at all for such beliefs.

After reading the above you will not be surprised to learn that the food and medicinal value of many of our most prized flowers were the qualities that first interested our forefathers. When tulips were introduced into Europe and England nearly five hundred years ago the bulbs were tried out both as food and as medicine. One writer stated that when "boyled and buttered they make a rare dish." Even as late as World War I, when food was scarce in Holland, tulip bulbs were used to some extent as food. They were found to be poor substitutes for normal foods, however.

The tulip, like the rose, is a plant whose history reaches far back into ancient time. When it first came into cultivation we

116

do not know, but we do know that the flower was enscribed on a pottery jar made about 2,000 years B.C., and it is believed that the Rose of Sharon mentioned in the Bible was actually the tulip.

A native of the lands at the eastern end of the Mediterranean, the tulip did not appear in northern Europe and England until about 1500. As proof of the great extent of tulip culture in Turkey there is in existence a manuscript written by Shiek Mohammed Lalizari—which means "tulip grower"—in which are listed 1,323 varieties of these flowers!

Tulips once actually caused a panic that threatened the finances of a nation. In the year 1634, the people of Holland began buying expensive tulip bulbs which cost as much as $1,200 each. Everyone bought tulip bulbs. Before long the prices of bulbs increased and then came wild speculation in the bulb market. It is said that at one time the price of a single bulb of the *Victory* variety was worth about $2,500. A bulb of the more expensive *Semper Augustus* variety once sold for $5,000 with a carriage and team of horses thrown in! In time people began to realize that the tulip market rested on a shaky foundation and within a few days tulip bulbs dropped in value and the tulip bubble burst, leaving the finances of Holland in a serious condition.

Holland is, of course, still famous for its tulip bulbs. At Limmen there is a "living museum" called the Hortus Bulborum where nearly a thousand varieties of tulips are grown. Many of these are kinds that have not been marketed for two hundred years. Tulip culture has long been a major industry in Holland, and it was there that the most expensive varieties were developed. The breeding up of new varieties is a very slow process, however, because from five to seven years are required to grow blooming tulips from seed.

Another flower with a long history is the lily. There are many different kinds of lilies in the world, but the one having the

117

longest and best known history is the Madonna or Easter lily, one of our most striking and best known cultivated flowers. The ancestors of this lily grew in the Iran region and were planted in gardens at least 3,000 years B.C. In fact, the name of the ancient city of Susa really means "The Lilies." Considered to be a sacred flower in very ancient times, the lily became associated with the Virgin Mary during the Christian era, which accounts for its present name. Some authorities believe that this snow-white lily was brought to Europe and England by the returning Crusaders, but this may not be true since it apparently was grown in Germany several hundred years *before* the time of the Crusades. Down the ages the Madonna lily has appeared on the coats-of-arms of many English families, probably as a symbol of purity.

Thus, we see that flowers have long been associated with man. They were carefully tended and bloomed in the royal gardens of ancient kings and were often taken away to new,

The breeding of tulips from seed requires five to seven years. This cut-away shows a tulip pistil and stamens with pollen-covered anthers.

The Madonna or Easter lily has long been considered a symbol of purity. Its ancestors grew in Iran and it has been cultivated in gardens for more than 5,000 years.

far lands by conquering armies. Here they grew and bloomed, adding their touches of beauty and color to gardens and courtyards.

Flower perfumes, too, as we have seen, have had their place in human history. Down the centuries the perfumer's art has blended flower fragrances of endless variety. Our ancestors used dried lavender petals to fill sweet-scented sachets, and petals were often scattered in clothes and linens, just as they are today.

Phlox flowers received their name from the Greek word for "flame." The name refers to the bright red coloration of some varieties.

CHAPTER 9

For Each a Name

There are about 250,000 different kinds of flowering plants in the world, and botanists have an exact scientific name for each one. These scientific or botanical names are usually in either Latin or Greek and are used and understood by botanists the world over. Common names are perfectly satisfactory for ordinary usage in our daily contacts with plants and flowers, but serious students must have more precise names. We may speak, for example, of geraniums, but the truth is that there are several different kinds of these common flowers, and botanists need to know exactly which kind is meant.

I can think of no better way of illustrating the value of scientific names than to relate an incident that occurred while I was in the South Pacific during World War II. There I found myself on a strange tropical island surrounded by beautiful and interesting flowering plants. Unfortunately, I had no books to help me identify them. Then one day in an abandoned house I found a book on the local flora. It was profusely illustrated with excellent pictures, but I was disappointed to find that it was written in Japanese. As I thumbed through the book, however, I found that beneath each picture, in fine print, was the scientific name, the same name that would identify it in an English book—or any other—on flowers. Thus, I could read the names and use the pictures to help me identify the local flowers.

This was certainly a stroke of luck, and it points up the value of scientific names which are, of course, the international language of all botanists and zoologists.

Too, common names are often confusing since the same name may be applied to several different flowers. For example, there are about a dozen entirely different plants and flowers that are called adder's tongues. The dog's-tooth violet—which is actually a true lily—is often called an adder's tongue. Other flowers bearing this same common name are one kind of yarrow, an arum, a geranium, and several kinds of orchids. There are also many cases where the same flower is designated by several different common names. This is often very confusing to a person attempting to identify a flower.

Most people are frightened away from scientific names largely because they do not understand them. Actually, the science of plant classification is not very complicated. Let us see how it works. The plant kingdom is divided into a number of groups or *classes*. For example, the liverworts, mosses, ferns, pines and flowering plants are each assigned to a separate class. Each class, in turn, contains a number of *orders,* and each of these is then divided into several *families*. Each family is divided into one or more *genera* (singular, *genus*). Each of these genera contains, in turn, one or more *species*.

Now let us see how this works out in actual practice. We will take a violet as an example. Violets belong to the *Angiospermae* class which includes all the flowering plants. They belong to the *Parietales* order. Examples of other orders of flowering plants are *Rosales,* the roses; *Geraniales,* the geraniums; *Cactales,* the cacti; and *Gentianales,* the gentians.

Tracing our violet on down through the scheme of classification we find that it belongs to the *Violaceae* family, a group that contains all the true violets. There are many different kinds of violets, however, and we find that our specimen belongs to the *Viola* genus. But it is not enough for a botanist to know that it is a violet; he must know what particular *kind* of violet. So we continue on down in our step-by-step classification and find that it belongs to the species *sylvatica*, a Latin name meaning that it is found in the woods. Now the botanical name consists of the genus and species, so we write the name for this special kind of violet, *Viola sylvatica*. Simple? In another instance we might find that a violet was named *Viola alba*. Obviously, this would be a white violet since *alba* means "white."

If we compare this method of plant or flower naming with human names we find one important difference. The names are reversed. Suppose your own name is John Jones. This means that you are a member of the Jones family and that your parents named you John. Jones is, thus, the group or family name, and John is the individual. In the case of a botanical—or zoological—name, the group name is written first, followed by the individual name. Thus, if you were to use the scientific method of writing your name, it would be Jones John. Actually, our names do appear in this way in some cases, especially when several names are listed in alphabetical order as in a telephone directory. Also, Chinese names are written with the family name first, followed by the individual's name. In this respect they are like the scientific names of plants and animals.

To help you understand how a flower is identified and placed in its proper name category, let us see how a botanist would do it. Suppose we give him an unknown flower and watch how he goes about determining its identity.

Since it appears to be a typical flower, he knows at once that it belongs to the Class *Angiospermae* which, as we have already seen, contains all the true flowering plants. He then makes a careful study of the flower under a hand lens, noting the general details of its structure, the number and arrangement of the stamens, pistils, petals and other parts. Having done this he finds that the flower belongs to the Order *Rosales*, a flower tribe which includes many groups of flowers—roses, sedums, hydrangeas,

If you had to name this flower, what would you call it? Probably "elephant's-head," and that is its name. The tiny red blooms grow on a stalk in wet places at high altitudes on western mountains.

witch hazels, plums, peaches, apples, peas, clovers, and mimosas.

He must next determine to which of these groups this unknown flower belongs. This will take a more detailed study of its parts. Through his hand lens he notes the number of stamens and where they are attached to the calyx. He sees, also, that there is a special arrangement of the pistils and of the ovaries which contain the ovules or developing seeds. He also makes notes on the leaf arrangement on the stem. From these structural details he decides that the flower belongs to the Family *Rosaceae* or rose family. He has now eliminated the peas, clovers, mimosas, sedums, hydrangeas and witch hazels which

124

belong to other flower families. However, the rose family is quite large and contains several different groups of flowering plants including roses, pears, apples, plums and raspberries, so his next step is to determine to which of these the unknown flower belongs. This will require an even more detailed study. He looks again at the flower parts and the leaves and stem and finds that the flower fits best the description of the Genus *Rosa*. All the true roses belong in this group, so he now knows that the unknown flower is a rose—but which one? There are many kinds of roses, and determining the exact one is going to take some more study. Now he must even take into consideration such things as habitat and geographical location. Noting down all these details he finds, at last, that the flower we gave him is a Carolina rose whose botanical name is *Rosa carolina*.

From the above we see that, starting out with all the flowering plants, a botanist eliminates them step by step down through the five stages of classification until he arrives at the scientific or botanical name. When botanists set out to identify any flower they follow this same step-by-step procedure. Of course, a pro-

The name for our common dandelion comes from France where it was called dent-de-lion, *meaning "teeth of the lion." This name refers to the toothed leaves.*

fessional botanist usually skips over most of the first steps since he usually recognizes at a glance to which general group a flower belongs.

So you see, scientific names are not really very complicated after all.

Most scientific or botanical names have very definite meanings and usually describe something about the flowers or about the plants that bear them. This is especially true of species names. Sometimes the name refers to size. *Nana* means "dwarf," *gigantea* means "large," while *alta* means "tall." Sometimes the name indicates color; *rubra* means "red," and *alba* means "white." Other colors may be indicated by *flava* meaning "yellow," *aureus* meaning "golden," or even *nigra* meaning "black" or "dark."

Sometimes even the scents of flowers are indicated by their names; *fragrans* means "fragrant," and *foetida* means "ill-scented." In some cases botanists have attempted to tell something about plants' habitats when they named them. Thus, we have *arvensis*, "growing in fields"; *palustris*, "growing in swamps"; *aquatica*, "growing in water"; or *sylvatica*, "woods dwelling." In a few cases we find clues to a plant's value to humans. *Esculentus* or *edulis* means that it is used as food; *sativus*, that it is grown as a crop; or *officinalis*, that it has medicinal value. You will also find that these scientific names often give hints as to the season of blooming. Thus, *vernalis* means "spring," *aestivalis* means "summer," while *autumnalis* obviously means that it grows or blooms in autumn. Some names indicate the original homes of the plants. For example, *sinensis* or *chinensis* means that it is of Chinese origin; *africanus*, that it came from Africa; or *japonicus*, that it came from Japan. One kind of rose, as we have seen, is named *Rosa carolina*.

Now it may surprise you to learn that, even though you may not be a botanist, you often use scientific names for flowers without knowing it. This is true, especially, of genus names. Lots of these names are simply the ancient names for the flowers and often have no meanings beyond that. The word, lily, is derived from *lilium*, a Latin name for this flower that originally came from Greek. Other names that were derived directly from ancient Latin and Greek are *Smilax, Cassia, Viola, Verbena, Vibernum, Rosa* and *Ambrosia. Ambrosia* was the mystical food of the gods. The name is now applied to plants of the ragweed group. A large number of the Latin and Greek flower names refer to their fancied resemblance to some object. Thus, we have *Sagittaria*, meaning that the plant's leaves are "arrow-shaped"; *Hydrangea*, from a fancied resemblance of its seeds to an ancient water vessel; *Geranium*, meaning "crane," referring to the flower's beak-like fruit; *Cornus* (dogwood), which means "horn-like" in reference to its hard wood; and *Crotalaria*, meaning "a rattle," from the loose seeds in its pods.

Our pretty *Delphiniums* received their name because of a supposed resemblance to dolphins. They are also called larkspurs which is, perhaps, closer to what they actually look like. Then, of course, we have *Aster*, the Greek word for star, and *Campanula*, meaning "little bell" in Latin. *Iris* was named for Iris, goddess of the rainbow, which is certainly appropriate. Iris blooms have a shimmering changeability in sunlight and it is from this quality that we get the word "iridescent." Another common flower whose ancient name we still use is *Digitalis* from the Latin *digitale*, meaning "finger of a glove." Our more often used name for this attractive flower is foxglove. Another common flower bearing an interesting name is lupine, but few people know that this name comes from the Latin word *lupus* meaning "wolf." You may not see much connection until you learn that our ancestors believed that this plant "devoured" the nourishing elements out of the soil. Among our most common small flowers is *Ranunculus*, a Latin word meaning "small frog." The flower was given this name because of its habit of growing in marshy situations.

Delphiniums were so named because it was thought they resembled dolphins. The more common name, larkspur, fits the flower better.

The name *Oxalis* is derived from Greek, meaning "sour," which has reference to its acid juice. Lavender is the name of a flower as well as the name of a color, but the name actually comes from the Latin word *lavendula*, meaning "to wash." Sweet-scented lavender was once used in the bath.

Other scientific names that are in common use originated through the practice of naming flowers after people. For instance, we have *Magnolia*, named in honor of Pierre Magnol who was a professor of botany at Montpellier University in southern France. *Poinsettia* received its name from Joel Poinsette who was once United States ambassador to Mexico. *Tradescantia* (spiderwort) was named for John Tradescant, gardener for

Charles I of England. Those common inhabitants known as zinnias owe their name to Johann Gottfried Zinn, an eighteenth century German professor.

Many of our most fanciful flower names are of Greek origin. For instance, *Phlox* means "flame," *Anemone* means "a flower shaken by the wind," and *Heliotropium* (Heliotrope) means "turning toward the sun." *Chrysanthemums* certainly look like "golden flowers" and that is just what the Greek name means.

From the Romans we received the name for our common *Nasturtiums* which comes from two Latin words, *nasus,* "nose," and *turqueo,* "to *twist,*" in reference to their pungent perfume. Also from Rome comes the name of our common *Gladiolus,* so named because of the resemblance of its sword-like leaves to the *gladius,* a short sword used by gladiators.

Tracing flower names back to their origins turns up interesting facts. Our common tulip was once grown only in Turkey. Credit for introducing this flower to the western world goes to a man by the name of Busbequius, who served as Austrian ambassador to the Sultan of Turkey. When he returned to Vienna in 1554 he brought the tulip and knowledge of its culture with him.

Roman gladiators used a short sword called a gladius *in the arena. The leaves of the gladiolus are shaped something like this sword and, hence, the name.*

They were then called tulipans, from the Turkish word *tülbend* meaning "turban." If one turns a tulip upside-down it is easy to see why it is named thus.

Some plants and flowers were named by our ancestors as a result of strange twists of fact and superstition. Such a case is *Scabiosa* or Devil's bit. The term *Scabiosa* comes from the use to which the plant was put during that period in history when "scabies" or itch was a common affliction. The other name, Devil's bit, has an even more curious origin. Many times these plants are found with their roots neatly severed just beneath the surface of the ground. This characteristic gave rise to the superstition that the Devil, annoyed by the good the plant did in ministering to human ailments, bit off its roots.

Our ancestors tried many common plants as cures for diseases; some were helpful and some were not. Some of the names given the plants suggest their original medicinal use. For example, there are several plants called "snakeroot." Others are named "selfheal" and "boneset." In early colonial days there was an Indian herb doctor named Joe Pye. One of his favorite cures was a medicine made of a common member of the daisy family known to botanists as *Eupatorium*. As you might expect, this plant is now popularly called Joe-Pye weed.

Almost every flower has a common as well as a botanical name and the origins of many of them make stories in themselves. During the crusades, so the legend goes, the crusaders brought back to England the roots of a yellow flower that became popular in that country. In honor of the Virgin Mary, people called this flower Mary's Gold, and the name eventually was shortened to marigold. The hollyhocks owe their name to two old English words *holi* and *hocke*, meaning holy "hock" or mallow plant. Most people probably think that the name for candytuft flowers has something to do with their resemblance to some sort of candy, but this is not so. These attractive flowers actually owe their name to their place of origin, the Island of

Columbine received its name from a fancied resemblance of its bloom to a group of doves with their heads toward the center. In this picture of a columbine bloom turned upside-down, you can see these five white "doves." The Latin word columbinus *means "dovelike."*

Crete. The ancient name for this island was Candia. Thus, it is a "tufted flower from Candia."

Another flower with a fanciful name is the columbine. If you will turn a columbine bloom upside-down and use your imagination you will see what appear to be five pretty birds huddled together with their heads toward the center. Now the Latin name for this flower is *columbinus*, meaning "dove-like." The "birds" that make up this attractive bloom are rather longnecked for doves, but perhaps that much imagination is permissible. Another fanciful name is pansy, a word derived from the French word *pensé*, meaning "thoughtful." The story behind this name is that, to the early French gardeners, the blooms looked like thoughtful little faces. From France, also, comes the name dandelion, where it was originally called *dent-de-lion* or "teeth of the lion," referring to the toothed leaves. And we should certainly mention the *fleur-de-lis*, another flower name of French origin. This, of course, is a classical name for the iris, but it was originally called *fleur-de-Louis*.

The names of some flowers are a little confusing. Many of us are familiar with cowslips and often call them by this name even though the name appears to make little sense. If, however, we pronounce it "cow's lip," as was originally intended, it makes more sense. The name refers to the shape of the petals.

A number of flowers received their names from ancient Greek mythology. An example is narcissus. It was, so mythology states, the youth Narcissus who, seeing his reflection in a pool, fell so in love with his own image that he pined away and was changed into the flower that bears his name.

Thus, out of the dim mists of the past have come the flower names used by both gardener and botanist. Each name has a story behind it.

Pansy blooms looked like thoughtful little faces to French gardeners. Their name comes from the French word pensé, meaning "thoughtful."

The name for narcissus comes from ancient Greek mythology. The youth Narcissus saw his reflection in a pool and fell in love with his image. He was changed into the flower.

The onion, believe-it-or-not, belongs to the lily family.

Their Family Tree

$\mathcal{I}$t is difficult for us to imagine a world without flowers; they seem so much a part of our everyday lives. Still, if we could, by some sort of magic, turn back the calendar of time a couple of hundred million years, we would find ourselves living at a period in the Earth's history when there were no flowers at all. Geologists have named this period in time the *Paleozoic Era,* meaning "ancient life." Suppose we take an imaginary walk through one of these Paleozoic forests. Our first feeling is that we have traveled to Mars, since the vegetation is so unlike any we have ever seen. There are huge "trees" a hundred feet tall and with trunks two or three feet in diameter, but they are far different from ordinary trees of today. Something about them seems familiar, however; then we realize that they appear to be huge ferns, club mosses and horsetails or scouring rushes. Actually, most of these plants are quite similar, and are related, to the ones we know in the modern world. But what a difference in size! Modern horsetails are hardly two feet tall, sometimes less. Yet here in this primeval forest their many-branched stems reach a hundred feet into the sky. Back home, when we take a stroll through a forest our feet tread upon a carpet of green mosses, but here the mosses are enormous "trees," and we feel like tiny ants creeping through a leafy jungle.

We walk on through this strange forest, but we see no butter-

135

cups or violets, or any other flowers. In all this ancient world there is not a single bloom of any kind. It is all a monotonous green. We eventually come to a small woodland lake and are surprised to see large, clumsy, frog-like creatures slithering about its muddy margin. Suddenly, however, we see a familiar sight. It is a dragonfly darting over the water in pursuit of gnats or flies—but what a dragonfly! It is over a foot-and-a-half across, but otherwise quite similar to those that dart over ponds or perch on twigs in modern times. For some strange reason, not fully understood by scientists, many of the plants and animals of the Paleozoic and later Eras grew to tremendous size. In many ways it was an age of giants.

By studies of the fossilized remains of the plants and animals that lived in those far-off years, scientists have learned a great deal about them. These fossils are the clues to the past. After the Paleozoic Era came to a close, the ancient world slowly changed as the Earth rolled on through space. Climates varied, and the land slowly arose and then sank again. Mountains were pushed up and then worn down again by rushing streams carrying sediments down to lakes and oceans. These sediments buried and preserved the remains of the plants and animals that had lived.

At this period in time there dawned in the world a new era called the *Mesozoic*, meaning "middle life." It was, perhaps, the most interesting time of all. Gone were the forests of ferns and club mosses. Instead there were extensive growths of a new kind of trees, the ancestors of our modern pines and other conifers. There were also tree-ferns. This age also saw the coming of the giant reptiles, the dinosaurs that ruled the world for many millions of years and then quite suddenly disappeared. But this period was important for at least two other reasons. Soon after its beginning the flowering plants appeared, followed, eventually, by the warm-blooded mammals that became the ancestors of horses, cattle, mice and monkeys. But strangely, in a world where almost everything was big, these ancient mammals were

The ancestors of the flowering plants, such as ferns and mosses, had no colorful blooms. They reproduced by spores instead of seeds. Then the pine and pinelike plants that produced seeds came into being, and from these came the true flowering plants. Very early the family tree divided. One branch produced the parallel-veined plants such as iris, lily, palms, grasses and orchids. From the other branches came the net-veined plants, including oak, primrose, violet, nightshade, pea, cactus, rose and daisy.

all quite small. The horses and camels were no larger than house cats, and there were primitive rhinoceroses the size of pigs. Even the ancestors of the elephants were small—hardly larger than a St. Bernard dog! Climates fluctuated from warm to cool and back to warm again, giving stimulus, perhaps, to the great changes that were occurring in both the plants and the animals. It was also a time of mountain formation; it saw the rise of great mountain chains, including the Rockies and the Andes. It was a time of eventful periods of change.

No one knows for sure just which plants were the real ancestors of the flowering plants, but it is believed that they were evolved from the ancient seed-ferns. By the close of the Mesozoic period the flowering plants were in great abundance and had spread to all the continents, ranging from the Tropics to the Arctic regions. Strangely, with the increased abundance of the flowers there came a decline in the pines and other conifers. These latter have never, of course, disappeared, but they have never again become as abundant as they once were during the early years of the Mesozoic. As this age slowly drew to a close, there was another event, as we shall see, that was most important from the standpoint of the flowering tribe.

Most of the flowering plants looked very much like modern kinds, and they were beginning to depend more and more on insects for pollination. There were buttercups, magnolias and tulip trees, as well as willows, elms, oaks, palms and maples. At this point in flower ancestry, however, a crossroad was reached and the clans divided. The plant families mentioned above continued on, changing a little as the ages passed. But now a new family branch came into being, the parallel-veined tribe. This branch of the flower family tree slowly developed down the centuries, eventually giving rise to modern arums (jack-in-the-pulpits), palms, air-plants, lilies, irises, grasses, cattails, bananas, and, at long last, those aristocrats of the flowers, the orchids. Certainly, it was a long road that led from the seed-ferns to the

In the bloom of this air-plant, which belongs to the parallel-veined tribe of flowering plants, the anthers and pistil peep out of the tightly wrapped bracts. These bracts are often very colorful, occurring in many pale shades and bright hues.

modern orchids, and it required more than two hundred million years for the plants to travel up it. Knowing this should make us appreciate the beauty of orchids even more.

In its long history the world has never remained the same for very long. During the next era more of the world's great mountain ranges were pushed up and the climates were cooled periodically by ice sheets advancing from the polar regions. This geological period has been named the *Cenozoic Era*, meaning "recent life." It began about fifty million years ago and is still going on. At the beginning of the Cenozoic the great dinosaurs had all passed away into ancient history and only the smaller reptiles remained. The mammal tribes were on the rise. It was— and is—the golden age of the flowers. The abrupt variations in the Earth's climates seemed to stimulate the production of flow-

The relationships of plants are determined largely by a study of their blooms. It may be difficult to believe that this tiny bluet belongs to the same family as the coffee tree.

ering plants in infinite variety. Flowers became more and more colorful and the relationships between them and the insects more complex. Some plants, like the grasses, that had once depended upon insect pollination gradually turned to the wind for help. In so doing, they lost the need for colorful petals, and at last their petals disappeared. On the other hand, many plants, such as the lilies, came to depend on insects even more and found need for larger and more brilliantly colored blooms to advertise their pollen and nectar.

Botanists look for clues to plant origins and relationships in their flowers. They study the number of flower parts and their arrangement. For example, as was mentioned earlier, the parallel-veined plants such as the lilies, orchids and irises have their petals, stamens and pistils in threes. If you cut an iris ovary open you will find that it, also, has three chambers or divisions. Thus, it is a rule that the flower parts of the parallel-veined tribe all are in threes or multiples of this number.

140

In the case of the great net-veined tribe there are usually more flower parts. If you count the stamens in a rose, for example, you will find that there are a large number. The same is also true of such flowers as strawberry, apple and buttercup. The flower parts of the net-veined tribe are usually in fives or multiples of that number. Both roses and buttercups are rather primitive as flowers go, and from them have descended many of our most common flowers. From the rose stock came the hydrangea and dogwood. From the dogwoods came the family branch that includes the carrot-like plants such as parsley. The common elderberry is also a descendant of the dogwood.

Sometimes it is a little difficult for us to understand the genealogies of flowers because the relationships are not very

The lilies developed from ancient ancestors. Lilies, irises, and their close relatives all have flower parts in threes or multiples of three. Note that this Easter lily has six stamens and a three-parted stigma.

obvious. A rose and a buttercup are rather similar and their relationship is plain to see, but more difficult to understand is the fact that both the walnut and the maple trace their descent back to the rose. Back beyond the rose, of course, are the buttercups, and from the ancient buttercups, also, arose the mallow family which includes the hollyhocks. From the mallows, in turn, came the geraniums, gentians and phloxes. Some of the phloxes' descendants developed two-lipped blooms and from them, in time, evolved the snapdragons, foxgloves and mints.

We have already seen that the orchids rank at the apex of those flowering plants having parallel-veined leaves. Among the net-veined tribes the asters, sunflowers and their relatives outrank all others in the evolutionary scale. This may seem strange since there are many flowers that seem far more colorful and complex than a daisy. Still, if we study the details of the daisies' floral structure, we realize that they do deserve the honor of top rating. If the flower head of a daisy or a sunflower is sepa-

Spanish moss is not really a moss but a member of the pineapple family. It belongs to the parallel-veined tribe.

The great sunflower tribe includes daisies, asters, zinnias, goldenrods, thistles and lettuce. Their flowers are made up of many tiny florets. Each is a complete flower, but only those around the outer edge have petals.

rated into its parts it will be found that it is not just one bloom but a cluster of blooms. These tiny blooms or individual flowers are packed tightly together and are called *florets,* each one complete with all the usual parts. Only the flowers around the margins have large, colorful petals. By this interesting arrangement the flower head is able to attract bees and butterflies with a minimum of colored petals. One row of petals advertises all the tiny florets in the head. Thus is the economy of Nature fulfilled. Of course, we speak of a sunflower or a daisy as a "flower" but actually it is many flowers or florets.

We have now followed the rise of the flowering plants, beginning with their primitive ancestors growing in the archaic forests. We have seen, briefly, how these flowers climbed the ladder of progress, step by step. Let us now go back and look more closely at the forces of nature that slowly created them. When we study flowering plants seriously we soon realize that their environments, or the conditions under which they have grown for long periods, have been like molds that gradually shaped them. They are, thus, products of their environments. Those fitted for life in their environments survived; those that were not disappeared.

The study of plants and animals in relation to their environment is called *ecology.* It is a relatively new science, but a fascinating one. Ecologists divide the areas where plants grow into a number of categories. For example, there are deserts, marshes, forests, plains (grasslands) and tropical forests. Let us see, briefly, some of the ways in which the flowering plants have adapted themselves to these various situations.

Perhaps the most interesting ecological situations are found in the deserts, and the desert habitat will illustrate very nicely how plants are molded by the conditions under which they live. Deserts are very exacting. They are regions of extremely low rainfall or of rainfall occurring over very short periods of the year. In our own Southwest, the deserts are very beautiful in

144

spring when all the various kinds of cacti deck themselves out in colorful blooms. Plants that live in these desiccated environments must adapt themselves to growth with very little moisture or be able to store up moisture to last during long periods of drought. Deserts, of course, cannot support a luxuriant vegetation; the plants that exist there are scattered trees and shrubs, and, of course, cacti and cactus-like plants. If you have ever driven across southern Arizona you have had opportunity to see good examples of true desert vegetation. (Arizona, by the way, means "arid zone.") One especially interesting thing you will notice is that the shrubs that cover the landscape in many places are evenly spaced as if they had been planted by human hands. Why? For the simple reason that the desert plants can only grow as close together as their roots can reach. There is not enough water in the soil to support more than one plant at a time. If, for example, the roots extend outward from the plant in a circle ten feet in diameter, then the plants will all be almost exactly twenty feet apart. This is the way deserts limit the density of vegetation and thus conserve moisture. Most interesting, however, are the measures taken by desert plants to store up moisture or prevent its loss. A great majority of the plants that thrive in deserts have greatly reduced leaf areas and the leaves are often thickened and filled with stored water. Sometimes, as in the cacti, there are no leaves at all, the work of photosynthesis or food manufacture being carried on by thick, green stems. This discussion, it might appear, has taken us far afield, but there is an important conclusion that can be drawn from the remarkable adaptations of desert plants. A desert is an excellent example of the way in which a special environment "molds" the plants that grow there. When we think of deserts we usually visualize a region of sand covered with cacti. In many cases this is true. There are many cacti on American deserts, but the remarkable thing is that the true cacti occur only in America. South Africa, also, has many desert-like areas in which grow numerous plants that resemble cacti, but they are not real cacti at all. They are plants of other families that the desert has "molded" to its way of life. The flowering plants that exist on Africa's dry, rocky slopes are often of wierd shapes. Sometimes they are spiny; at other times they mimic the coarse gravel among which they live. One kind looks like plover eggs. Probably the most common of these African desert "cacti" belong to the spurge or *Euphorbia* family which also contains our common poinsettia and snow-on-the-mountain. These desert *Euphorbias* are very cactus-like and have attractive blooms. Sometimes, like true cacti, they are protected by vicious spines. Botanists are only able to tell that they are not real cacti by studying their flowers.

But it is not only the *Euphorbia* tribe that the African desert has shaped to its needs. It may surprise you to learn that even some members of the daisy or sunflower clan, too, have developed thick leaves and cactus-like stems and taken up a desert abode. Examples are some of the African *Senecios* that would certainly fool you into thinking they are cacti. At certain seasons, however, they produce attractive orange blooms, and it is only then that botanists realize they are first cousins to our

Stonecrops (Sedums) and pincushion cactus of our western prairies are well adapted to regions of deficient moisture.

True cacti are found only in America. African "cacti" actually belong to other plant families that have changed their forms to fit the dry desert conditions.

common asters. There are a number of other flowering plant families, such as the milkweeds, that have "banished" some members of their tribes to the deserts.

Thus does the desert shape her flowering plants to life in an environment where only the especially fitted can survive. Other environments, too, have rather precise requirements. The flowers that grow in forests, marshes and prairies all must meet certain specifications. This is evolution in action. The flowering plants we have today are all the end results of slow environmental "pressures" down millions of years of growth and natural selection. The flowers have slowly climbed up the family tree.

147

Index

Page numbers in italics are those on which illustrations appear.

Agave, 13
Air-plant, 138, *139*
Alder, 66, 73
Allard, H. A., 88
Ambergris, 106
Anemone, 16
Anemophilous flowers, 61
Angiospermae, 122, 123
Annual plants, 13
Anther, 12, 17, *62*, 118, 139
Anthocyanin, 28
Apple, 22
Aristolochia, 55, 56
Arum, 27, 57, 138
Aspen, 67
Aster, 88, 142
Azalea, *50*

Bamboo, 85
Banana, 138
Barberry, 48
Bean, 88
Bees
   in pollination, 22-25
   sense of smell, 108, 109
Beet, 13
Beetle flowers, 109
Bergamot, 104
Biennial plants, 13
Birch, 73
Bladderwort, 51
Blooming, time of, 85-99
Bluet, *140*
Bract, 16, *139*
Bryophyllum, *15*, 16
Buckeye, 83
Buckwheat, 88
Bumblebee, 23, *24*
Buttercup, 19, 138, 142
Butterflies
   colors of, 31

pollination by, 25, *45*, 46
Butterfly weed, 33

Cabbage, 13
Cactales, 122
Cactus, 122, 145, *146*, *147*
   blooms, 39
   prickly pear, 48
   queen-of-the-night, 39
Caladium, 57
Calla lily, 57
Calopogon, 54
Calyx, 17
Camas, death, 83
Candytuft, 130
Carnation, 103
Carotene, 29
Catalpa, 51
Cattail, 138
Cenozoic Era, 139-142
Century plant, 13, 32
Cereus, 39-40
Chicory, 28
Chlorophyll, 29
Chrysanthemum, 88, 92, 93, 129
Clover, red, 22
Cocklebur, 88, 89, 93
Color
   as navigational aids, 37
   autumn, 27
   flower, 27-37
   night flowers, *39*
   of birds, 30, 31
   pigment, 30
   seen by insects, 35
   structural, 31
Columbine, 16, 41, *131*
Coreopsis, *87*
Corn, *62*
Corolla, 17
Cosmos, 88

Cotton, 22, 88
Cottonwood, 19, 67
Cowslip, 132
Cross-pollination, 22
Crucianella, 51
Cucumber, 88
Cycads, 71

Dahlia, 13
Daisy, 19, *34, 36*
  ox-eye, 36
Dandelion, 29, *125*
Darkness, effect on flowering, 90-94
Datura, *96, 97,* 101
Delphinium, 127, *128*
Desert vegetation, 144-147
Devil's bit, 130
Digitalis, 127
Doctrine of Signatures, 116
Dodder, 83
Dogwood, *17,* 88, 144
Dutchman's pipe, *55, 56*

Easter lily, 118, *119*
Ecology, 144
Eleagnus, 110
Eleanthus, 83
Elm, 73, 138
Equisetum, 60
Essences, flower, 102-106
Essential oils, 102
Eupatorium, 130
Euphorbia, African, 146
Eyes, insect, 33

False dragonhead, *91*
Fertilization, 21
Fire pink, *82*
Fleur-de-lis, 132
Flora, 111
Floralia, Festival of, 111
Floret, *36, 143,* 144
Florigen, 90
Flower
  ancestors, 135-147, *137*
  bird pollinated, 58
  class, 122
  clocks, 95
  color, 27-37
  effect of altitude, 98, 99
  families, 122

  heat production, 57
  imperfect, 19
  in ancient history, 111-116
  luminous, 40, 41
  moth pollinated, 38, 41
  names, 121-132
  parts of, 20
  perfect, 18
  perfumes, 101-119
  seen by insects, *34*
  shapes, 37, *38*
  size, 27
  time of blooming, 96-98
Four-o'clock, 16
Fox glove, 142
Fuchsia, 16

Gardenia, *104*
Gardner, W. W., 88
Gentian, 122, 142
Gentianales, 122
Geranium, 88, 122, 142
Ginkgo, 20, 67, 71
Gladiolus, *129*
Goldenrod, 29, 88
Grass, 20, 138, 140
  pollination, *63,* 64
Grasse (France), 102

Habenaria, 54
Hayfever, 71, 76, 77
Heliotrope, 129
Hibiscus, 28
Hollyhock, 130, 142
Honeybee, 23, 25, *43*
  eye, *33*
Honeysuckle, 110
Horsetail, *60*
Huckleberry, *26, 81*
Hummingbird, 25, 32
Hydrangea, 127

Indoleascetic acid, 14
Indolebutyric acid, 14
Insect eye, 32
Iris, 16, 20, 127, 138, 140

Jack-in-the-pulpit, 57, *58*
Jasmine, 102
Jessamine, 83

About the Author

Entomologist Ross Hutchins is also an expert photographer, and this combination of interests has resulted in almost thirty years of studying, photographing and writing about insects, plants, animals and birds. Born in Montana, he grew up on a cattle ranch near Yellowstone Park. At Montana State College he majored in biological sciences and later he took his Ph.D. in zoology and entomology from Iowa State College.

Dr. Hutchins' articles and pictures of natural history subjects have appeared in encyclopedias, books and magazines, among them *National Geographic, Life* and *Natural History*, as well as such European publications as *Sie und Er, La Vie des Bêtes* and *Sciences et Avenir*. A special interest in unusual insect and plant life led to his own books in the juvenile field—INSECT BUILDERS AND CRAFTSMEN; INSECTS—HUNTERS AND TRAPPERS; STRANGE PLANTS AND THEIR WAYS; WILD WAYS; and THIS IS A LEAF.

Ross Hutchins now lives in Mississippi where he is Entomologist and Executive Officer of the Mississippi State Plant Board and head of the Department of Zoology and Entomology at Mississippi State University.